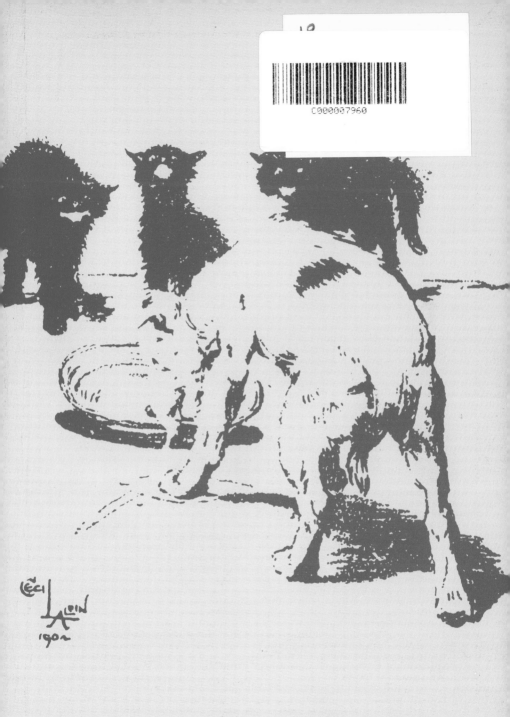

CÉCIL
ALDIN
1902

COLLECTING DOULTON ANIMALS

1900-1990

A COLLECTORS LIST COMPILED BY
JOCELYN LUKINS

Cat 203	Rabbits 209	Rooster 164
Wilfred 922	Butterflies 162	Owl 187
Terrier 1099	Fox K34	Mouse 226
Collie 105	Toucan 159	Cat 109

Back

Peke 1011	Penguins 133	Tiger 912
Duck 229 Drake 116	Fox 100	Budgies 199, 163
Elephants 181, 2644		Lion 1086
Cocker 1001	Bulldog 4607	Fox 963

Front

The products listed and shown were originally manufactured by Royal Doulton. The names *Doulton* And *Royal Doulton* and the backstamps shown are registered trade marks. This Book has been produced independently and Jocelyn Lukins has no connection with Royal Doulton.

© JOCELYN LUKINS 1990
ISBN 0 95 10288 3 9
PUBLISHED BY VENTA BOOKS

JOCELYN LUKINS photography Ventafile
The majority of photographs and illustrations in this book have supplied by Ventafile, a compilation of material and information assembled by Jocelyn Lukins.

CONTENTS

HN 1082 Courtesy Louis Taylor

INTRODUCTION

I'm a cat person myself and I'm indebted to my 'doggy' friends for infecting me with their enthusiasm, so that I am now at least an avid follower of the Crufts Show on television. Many dog breeders and dog lovers are also keen collectors of Royal Doulton *Championship* dog models as the modelling details and colouring are so authentic, they have helped me with many finer points. A friend of mine is a leading ornothologist and he has taught me quite a lot on woodland walks. I know just a little more than the painter at the Burslem factory who thought that by adding a red breast to the model of a wren it became an English Robin.

I've learned even finer points such as that in the Tern HN 167 and the Black Headed Gull HN 212, both male and female should have black heads. No doubt the marketing board thought that by painting them differently it was a way of selling the same model as a pair, so many Burslem animals come in loving pairs.

Robin HN 144
Wren Ashtray HN 1089

Black Headed Gulls
HN211 HN212

Someone also somewhere along the line, called them ducks and drakes, a term that only applies to wild ducks, but language was so prim in 1920. Many ducks in the range appear with drake's curly tails and models are catalogued as mallards, whether they are that breed or not, as the moulds are re-used and given a new colourway. My dog experts tell me that although you can use the Cairn HN 1033 mould as a West Highland Terrier HN 1048 it doesn't work when you use a Bull Terrier HN 1142 mould and call it a Staffordshire HN 1131.

However although these mistakes may make us feel superior in our own fields they are minor anomalies. I don't think any the less of Desmond Eyles's scholarship because in the list of animals he drew up for the first edition of *Royal Doulton Figures*, 1978, he called a *Collie* HN 105 an Alsatian or a *Wildebeest* HN 2507 a Zebra. That list is all we have had to help us in making a collection of animals to date and it has been invaluable. Katherine Morrison McClinton gave us more pictures and some information in *Royal Doulton Figurines and Character Jugs* 1978 but it has been very difficult so far to see the HN range of animals as a whole. Unfortunately I have been unable to use any other reference than Desmond Eyles for the central portion of my main list, if I have not found an actual model. Assuming his classifications are way off I have applied some common sense corrections. I have looked at animals in collections and taken details for ten years but I really feel I need at least another ten to complete the task so here I am calling on collectors to help. It would have been useful to have been able to consult the Doulton records for information but that has not been possible as there is another book in preparation. However I find one needs a combination of the company records, contempory catalogues and above all existing pieces in your collections. This book is a start, some information and some pictures. A second edition will follow in a very few years when the information and corrections are added with the help of vigilant friends.

Meanwhile 1990 is a very good year to make a stab at it as it marks the introduction of a new Royal Doulton animal range.

Collie HN105

6

ACKNOWLEDGEMENTS

The pleasure of my work is in the number of friends made around the world whilst trying to get information together. In quite a small collection Jeanette Morrisby in Australia found the only shire horse with the champions name *Punch Peon* HN 2623 stamped on the foot and a photograph of the elusive *Cocker and Hare* HN 1063. Susan Kasulka and Fred Dearden supplied me with details from very interesting U.S. catalogues. Nick Tzimas and Princess and Barry Weiss supplied me with photographs of some very rare items. Everyone has been so helpful. Thank you all so much:-

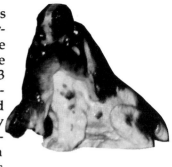

Cocker and Hare HN 1063

Diane Alexander, Jo-Ellen Arnold, Catherine Braithwaite, Ann Cook, Dave Cope, Tony Cross, Fred Dearden, Helen Fortune, Henry Gibbons, Heritage Antiques, Susan Kasulka, Jeanette Morrisby, Mr & Mrs L Merritt, Sheldon Merric, Elizabeth Nevell, Mark Oliver, Diane Petersen, Doug Pinchin, Tom Power, Ed Pry, Debbie Sawco, Joe Schenburg, Janet Secor, Mr & Mrs G Tanner, Nick Tzimas and Princess and Barry Weiss.
- not forgetting Henry who has learned not to sit on the page I am writing and has forgiven me when meals were late as time was forgotten in enthusiasm for the task.

Like Henry we should first take a look at some of the Lambeth Animals which had an influence on the Burslem range, the chief subject of this booklet.

Henry inspecting a fountain with modelled Herons and Frogs, 26" John Broad c.1875

ANIMALS AT LAMBETH

When John Doulton started his business at Lambeth in 1815 the factory was engaged in making utilitarian objects and one of them was probably the first Doulton animal. It was a flower holder in the shape of a hedgehog made about 1840, very rare, but they have one at the Museum of London. Animals soon played an important part in the Lambeth factory's history. They brought fame to the first two artists ever employed there, George Tinworth (1866) and Hannah Barlow (1871). Tinworth's whimsical frog and mice groups are much more sought after today than his monumental religious sculptures so lauded at the time.

Hannah Barlow had her own private zoo of over a hundred animals including a fox that followed her around like 'a well trained dog'. Although most of her animals were incised drawings on clay she did exhibit some important sculptures and modelled vases and plaques in very high relief. She studies her own animals and those at the zoological gardens but although a keen observer of animal anatomy, due to a nicety of the times, she never reproduced their 'private parts' and udders on her cows are extremely rare.

*Crossing the Channel George Tinworth 5"
c.1885
Courtesy Sotheby*

Hannah Barlow and Rufus Darwin her King Charles Spaniel 1913

Hedgehog 2" c.1840

*Kitty and her friends a terracotta group of a pony and rabbits 11"
Hannah Barlow c.1885 Courtesy Phillips*

Rhinocerous Leslie Harradine

At the turn of the century Chinese dragons were fashionable and many artists at Lambeth, Harry Barnard, Cund and John Broad amongst them, with Charles Noke at Burslem, added sinuous modelled dragons to their vases. Mark Marshall was especially good at

Flower centre with Donkey 6" John Broad 1879
Courtesy Richard Dennis

this and modelling other grotesque animals real or mythical. However fewer realistic animals were sculpted but there were examples like Tinworth's kangeroo and monkeys, Cund's monkeys, Leslie Harradine's rhinoceros and Mark Marshall's rabbits but the majority were artistic interpretations.

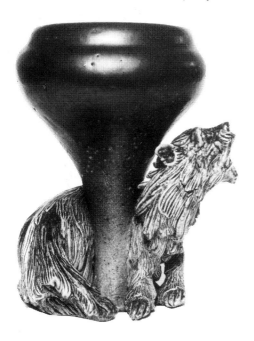

14 Vase with modelled Bear cub 10" Mark Marshall 1880s

Kangeroo 6" John Broad

The twentieth century brought a simpler approach and many more naturalistic animals were modelled. Harry Simeon liked bears and used them on ink wells and cruet sets and did other animals including a crowing cock, a drake and this Ibex bookend. Leslie Harradine before 1912, when he left Lambeth to farm in Canada, created this marvelous chimp, a sleeping spaniel and the cuddling monkeys which were later used in the Burslem range.

17 TR   *Chimpanzee 8" Leslie Harradine Courtesy Phillips*

16 TL   *Three Bears Silicon cruet set 3" Harry Simmeon c.1900*

18 ML   *Ibex bookend 5" Harry Simeon c.1925*

19 BL   *Rooster vase 5" Mark Marshall 1880s*

20 BR   *Rabbit 8" L Mark Marshall Courtesy Sotheby's*

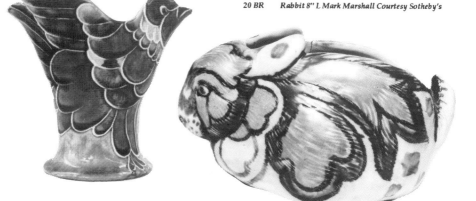

LESLIE HARRADINE

His slip cast models included polar bears, a cockatoo and a duckling group which had great appeal and sold in some numbers.

Cockatoos H 35 8"
Bear on a cube HN 119 and Lambeth version 4",
Two Apes and Spaniel H 7
Polar Bears H 56 8.5"
Ducklings H 5 4.5"
All c.1910

About 1920, John Broad produced a pair of Persian cats in a fine hardpaste porcelain but most animals were in the stoneware body which did not allow great detail but nevertheless surprising realism was acheived. Leslie Harradine, Frank Pope, Harry Simeon and Vera Huggins were responsible for a whole host of animals which appeared on bookends and pin trays when the 1930's came, an age of novelties or 'fancies' as they were known in the china trade. Richard Garbe's sea lions (1934) and Gilbert Bayes washing post top animals (1938) added to the zoo.

Bibilots - Koala, Night Heron and Butterfly trays c.4" 1930
Toucan on a rock 4"
Greyhound 20" Gilbert Bayes c.1930
Polar Bear, Mouse and Pelican trays c. 4" 1930 Courtesy Phillips
Owl bookend 6" Harry Simmeon c.1925 Courtesy Phillips

Fig. R22. Rabbit and young
7½" high, 14" long
18 -

Fig. R24. Duck
15" high
15 -

Fig. R29. Owl
14" high
15 -

Rtgd. No 744107
Fig. R18. The Elf
18¾" high × 6¾" overall
diameter
30 -

Fig. R21. Cat
16" high
15/-

Fig. R25. Hare. 24" long × 11" high
20/-

Regd. No 736048
Fig. R16. Fox. 16" high
22/6

There was even an exchange of animal models with the Burslem factory and in this Lambeth catalogue page of 1938, was can see how Harry Simeon translated the duck, the cat, the hare and the fox from Charles Noke's Burslem range into large terracotta garden ornaments.
In 1955 shortly before the closing of the Lambeth factory due to the passing of the Clean Air Act in 1956, Agnetta Hoy, Lambeth's last artist produced an appealing 10" tabby kitten in a very limited edition of about twelve copies. At the same time in Doulton's Burslem factory a comprehensive animal range was well established and producing thousands of fine china figures which we will review next.

The Waning of the Honeymoon 6"
Possibly Frank Pope

ANIMALS AT BURSLEM

Charles Noke inaugurated the HN Range of animals. From an early age he had been fond of modelling animals and there is a record of him doing so whilst still at school using clay borrowed from the Worcester factory which he often visited with his father. In 1874 aged sixteen he started work there under the guidance of a fine modeller Charles Binns. He worked mainly on figure modelling whilst at Worcester and in his early days at Doulton where he moved in 1889. One feels he must have relished the prospect of creating a whole animal range at Burslem in 1912.

Charles Noke modelled this and many other elephants of which he was particularly fond. Many large elephants were produced in flambe and Sung glazes but this is in a natural textured grey. HN 1121 13" c.1937. Courtesy Sotheby's

He had modelled some earlier than this for a *flambé* range introduced in 1908. The models shown in a contempory advertisement reappeared in the HN range. The *Lop-eared Rabbit* became HN 108, the *Mouse on a cube* HN 255, issued in 1921 and *three Fledglings* HN 280. Conversely many HN regular models received flambé glazes through the years such as HN 1115 the *Airdale* from the *Championship* dog series.

The Connoisseur 1912

Other animals were produced at Burslem prior to the introduction of the HN range. For instance the *Greyhound* HN 890 was first used as part of a vellum figure in the 1890's. The first animal in the HN range *Huntsman Fox* HN 100 has

a model number 151 and we can safely assume that any number lower that this can probably be found in a flambé glaze. The animals in the monochrome glazes of red, blue, chrome yellow, orange and black, all on earthenware bodies and slightly larger than their china counterparts in the HN range also seem to pre-date 1913 and have low model numbers. The two curled foxes are model 6 and the single one 15. The seated collie later HN 105 is model 47.

Diana lamp with greyhound 11" Vellum. Charles Noke 1890's.   *Two cuddling Foxes Treacle glaze 3.5" c.1910*

Animals in matt coloured glazes c.1910

Fledgling 4"

Bear HN 246 5"

Other animals in a semi-regular colouring such as this fledgling on a rock, and the bear and pig standing with arms folded were produced as early as 1910. In 1913 these models were gathered together and added to through the years. Different sizes and colourways were introduced. Some were very popular and were issued for decades. Others, todays rarities, had no life at all. The early animal models unlike the figurines were not influenced by fashion and trends in art sculpture. The animals reflected simple precepts like naturalism or whimsicality. Unfortunately throughout all the Noahs ark of animals created at Burslem we can attribute only a few to a particular modeller. We do know however that Charles Noke created the magnificent elephant models and the equally impressive lions, tigers and leopards of which there are examples in production to this day in the *Prestige* range. We also know he modelled the *Pedlar Wolf* HN 7 and the *'Granny' Owl* HN 173 and can therefore conclude he was probably responsible for some of the other character foxes and hares, monkeys and mice. He also had a team of talented artists under him capable of producing the wide range of these early years. Desmond Eyles mentions that it was thought Leslie Harradine submitted some of the bird models and remembering his Lambeth Cockatoos H 35 it seems very possible.

H.N. 197.   H.N. 163.   H.N. 133.   H.N. 205.   H.N. 158.

H.N. 116.   12. H.N. 147.   H.N. 125,   H.N. 176,   H.N. 151.

H.N. 117.   231, H.N. 168.   61. H.N. 802,

H.N. 181.   H.N. 27.   H.N. 128.   H.N. 134.   H.N. 132.

H.N. 276.   H.N. 161.   H.N. 118.   H.N. 280,   H.N. 137.   H.N. 145.

ROYAL DOULTON BIRDS AND ANIMALS.

Catalogue Page 1927

HN197	163	133	205	158	116	147	125	
HN176	151	117	168	802	181	27	128	
HN134	132	276	161	118	280	137	143	*HN205 Should Read 185*

His Polar bear on a cube and cuddling Monkeys made at Lambeth appear as HN 119 and HN 883 in the list as well as in flambé glazes. They probably all appeared concurrently too. Harradine's Polar bears on an ice floe H 58 produced at Lambeth c1912 might mean he was responsible for the many like subjects in the HN list (see page 10).

HN 131 / 163 / 132 / 149 / 158

Birds feature a lot in the early days, usually the least collectable of animal subjects. Foxes and pigs were always in evidence and are as collectable as ever today. There are always specialists in this field. I am a fox collector myself.

Dogs appeared in the list from the *Collie* HN 105 to the many character dogs, some representing definite breeds like the *Fox terrier* HN 944. When Frederick Dawes *Championship* series entered the field in 1931 with their wonderful realism, the dogs, obviously popular, took over. William Chance's realistically modelled horses introduced in 1940 were never as popular as the dogs.

Charles Noke we know was a dog lover and his son Jack, who followed him as Art Director in 1936, according to Peggy Davies was a cat lover. Luckily Peggy Davies mentioned some of the animals she modelled, but even she couldn't be sure of all. So many models are submitted and sometimes those are shelved for years. We know the artists involved with the art ranges but it is regrettable so many are unattributable as yet.

COLLECTING ROYAL DOULTON BURSLEM ANIMALS

In the collectors world of ceramic animals those of Royal Doulton stand out as some of the finest ever produced. The quality of the modelling, its authenticity and realism in the championship series is rarely surpassed by other factories. Added to the champion dog and horse series are many more realistically modelled animals from an elephant to a mouse and a whole host of whimsical and colourful character animals from the fox in hunting pink to miniature pigs in clown costume. In all over 800 animal models have been made by Royal Doulton between 1913 and 1990. A daunting number for most collectors but few people attempt them all. *Championship* dogs are the most collected with many specialising in a particular breed only. Elephant, fox and pig collectors abound and if you have other favorites you will probably find them in the range.

Unfortunately many of the early models and some issued just prior to the two world wars with very short runs are rare today. Also animal models seem to be particularly subject to damage due to the vicissitudes of time and stress inherent in the original moulds. So perhaps collectors should accept damage and restoration more readily in elusive pieces. There is no doubt that animals are worthy of a stronger place in the world of Doulton collecting and I hope this booklet will unite collectors around the world and that they will be joined by many newcomers to the field who hadn't realised what a fascinating assortment of collectables exist to claim their interest.

Pedlar Wolf HN 7, Pride of the Shires & Foal HN 2528, Pig Bowl HN 243, Alsatian HN 1022, Elephant HN 1123, The Chestnut Mare HN 2566, Fox Terrier HN 1013, Guinea Fowl HN 243, K1, Bulldog HN 1044, Cuddling Monkeys as HN 883. Courtesy Phillps

Group of birds HN 158 122 185 149 111 131 152

Group of ducks HN 807 299 2591 806 853 132

Fledglings HN137 145 143

Fledgling on rock in 3 colourways

DOULTON BURSLEM ANIMAL MODELS 1913-1990

HN		HT	MODEL	DATE
7*	*Pedlar Wolf*	7.5	76	1913-
100*	Fox in hunting dress	6	151	1913-42
101	Hare in hunting dress			
102	Hare in white coat			
103*	Two loving Penguins	6	133	
104*	Penguin	6	134	
105*	Collie seated - sable	8	47	
106	Collie seated - white/sable	8	47	
107	Hare hunched	2	119	
108	Rabbit - one ear up - white	4	113	
109*	Cat seated - white	5	9	
110	Butterfly bowl	3		
111*	Cockerel crowing on stand	3	25	
112	Collie seated	7.5	47	
113*	Penguin - sharp pointed beak	6	84	
114	Mallard Drake - green head	6	137	
115*	Mallard Drake - blue head	6	137	
116*	Mallard Drake - green back	6	137	
117*	Two Foxes curled together	4	6	
118*	Monkey - folded arms grey	3	53	
119*	Polar Bear on green cube	4	67	
120	Cat-sitting up grey/white	5	9	
121	Polar Bear - seated	3.5	39	
122*	Two fantail pigeons	4	46	
123*	Pelican beak out	6.5	109	1913-26
124*	Cockerel crouching - pale yellow	4	30	
125*	Guineau fowl - grey	3.5	69	
126*	Hare - brown	2	119	
127*	Peke looking up	3.5	82	
128*	Puppy seated	4	116	
129*	Bulldog seated	6	135	1917
130*	Fox seated	9	102	
131*	Kingfisher on brown rock	4	44	
132*	Drake on rock - turquoise head	3.5	138	
133*	Two loving Penguins	6	103	
134*	Penguin	4	85	
135*	Raven on rock	3	43	
136*	Swallow on brown rock	4.5	196	
137*	Fledgling on rock open beak	4	139	
138*	Squirrel	2	115	
139	Eagle on rock	9	145	
140	Ape head turned		147	
141*	Rhinoceros - grey. white horn	3.5	107	
142	Hare hunched (as 107)	2	119	
143	Fledgling crouched	2	123	1917-
144*	Robin. wren mould	2	104	
145*	Fledglings-various poses	2	98	1915-36
146*	Bulldog - tin hat & haversack	6.5		1918
147*	Foxes - 4 poses, 3 sizes		29	
148	Two ducks	2	112	
149*	Swallow on white rock	4.5	196	
150	Duck - head streched foward	4	207	

HN		HT	MODEL	DATE
151*	Rabbit - one ear up,	4	108	1918
152*	Kingfisher on rock	4	44	
153*	Bulldog - Tam o'Shanter	7		
154*	'Kateroo' by Souter	13	214	
155	Owl - green/brown	5	153	
156*	Monkey - hand to ear	3.5		
157*	Cockerel sitting	3		
158	Toucan on a rock - blue	8	212	
159*	Toucan on a rock - green	8	212	
160	Owl with owlet under wing			
161*	Four fledgling Thrushes in a row	2	161	
162*	Butterfly on a rock, blue/gold	3		
163*	Budgerigar on tree stump	7	221	
164*	Rooster crowing	9	225	
165*	Kingfisher flying to tree stump	3	227	
166	Foxhound seated	4	209	
167*	Tern - female	2.5	231	
168*	Tern - male	2.5	231	
169	Owl - brown	3		
170	Bear			
171	Four fledglings - 3rd one higher	2		
172*	Bison	5		
173*	Owl in red cloak & ermine collar	8	228	
175	Great Crested Grebe			
176*	Bloodhond seated	6	48	
177	Grotesque on bowl	4		
178*	Cockerel crouching	4	30	
179*	Two Foxes curled together	4	117	
180*	Tockerel crouching	4	30	
181*	Elephant - trunk down, curled	4		
182	Monkey - green jacket & hat	7	213	
183*	Monkey - blue jacket & hat	7	213	
184*	Rooster crowing	9	225	
185*	Cockatoo on rock	6	68	
186*	Elephant - grey (as 181)	4		
187*	Owl - grey check shawl,	8	228	1919
188	Duckling sitting up - yellow	3	3	
189	Duckling - black/yellow	3	3	
190	Duckling - green/blue	3	3	
191	Cockatoo on rock - blue/purple	6	68	
192	Cockatoo on rock - red/orange	6	68	
193*	Tortoise - red head, grey shell	2	101	
194*	Puppy dog - lying down	3	121	
195*	Gannet	7	243	
196	Toucan in tail coat		212	
197	Birds - black with orange breast	6	251	
198*	Penguin with chick	5.5	239	
199*	Budgerigar on tree stump	7	221	
200*	Cockatoo on a tree stump	6	68	
201*	Cat with mouse on tail - tabby	5	216	
202	Cat with mouse on tail - black	5	216	
203*	Cat on pillar - tortoiseshell	4	240	
204*	Persian Cat - looking up	5	242	
205	Two Ducklings - black/white	2.5	247	
206	Two Ducklings - brown/white	2.5	247	

Pekinese HN127 826 927 1012

Bird and 5 chicks HN272 Hare HN126 273

Lion HN1086 Tiger HN912 Elephant HN2644

Pheasant Cock HN2632 Hen HN2610

HN		HT	MODEL	DATE
207	Mouse in smock		250	1919
208	Toucan in tail coat and bow tie		234	
209	Two Rabbits - cuddling	3.5	249	
210	Cat sleeping -black/white	1.5	23	-36
211*	Black headed Gull - male	4	235	
212*	Black headed Gull female -	4	236	
213*	Two Pigs - one up, one down	3.5	61	
214	Birds, 5 chicks, black/pink/brown -		4	
215	Birds, 5 chicks, grey/blue/lemon -	4		
216	Birds, 5 chicks, green/blue/lemon -	4		
217	Two Rabbits cuddling	3.5	249	
218*	Two Rabbits cuddling -	3.5	249	
219	Two Rabbits cuddling	3.5	149	
220	Birds on rock - red/brown	4	251	
221*	Persian Cat - looking up,	5	242	
222*	Owl in moon shaped dish	4		
223*	Lion sitting up - brown	6.5		
224	Kingfisher on rock -	3.5	258	
225*	Tiger crouching - brown	2	111	
226*	Town Mouse in blue coat	2.5	230	
227	Cat sleeping-head on paw	1.5	23	
228	Town Mouse in yellow coat	2.5	230	
229*	Mallard Duck head foward	4	207	
230	Drake - round base	4		
231*	St Bernard seated	8		
232*	Puppy seated	4	118	
233*	Cat lying	3.5	70	
234*	Two loving Cats	5	259	
235	Comic Duck - orange/black	2.5		
236	Two Chicks	2.5	263	
237	Character Mouse, apron & basket			
238	Two Pigs	3.5	61	
239*	Two Ducks	5.25L	97	
240	Tropical Birds with grasses			
241	Eagle crouching on rock	9	265	
242	Eagle crouching on rock	9	265	
243*	Pig bowl brown/white	3.5		1919-36
244	Cat on pillar black/white	4	240	1919-36
245	Cat on pillar black	4	240	
246	Pig with folded arms	5		1910-36
247*	Guineau Fowl on rock	3.5		
248	Drake white L		307	
249	Mallard Drake head up L		307	
250	Heron flower centre		314	
251	Heron flower centre		314	
252	Drake - white		307	
253	Monkey seated	3		
254	Monkey mother and child	2.5	52	
255*	Mouse on cube	2.5	1164	1921
256-66	Character Penguins & Puffins	1	328	
267	Cockerel sitting			
268	Kingfisher			
269	Blue Birds on rock			
270*	Bear sitting up - brown	5	88	
271	Duck			

HN		HT	MODEL	DATE
272*	Birds with 5 chicks, jade green	3.5		1929
273*	Hare crouching - yellow	2	119	
274	Birds - green			
275	Two Birdss - orange			
276	Rabbit one ear up -	4	113	
277	Wren			
278	Two Birdss - green/yellow	2		
279	Birds on rock - green			
280*	3 chicks in a row, yellow	2		
281	Birds on rock - yellow			
282	Birds - blue			
283-93	Character Penguins & Puffins	1.5		
294	Toucan - black/white	8		
295	Toucan - black/white	8		
295a	Toucan - black/white	8		
296	Penguin			
297*	Penguin and chick	5.5	239	
298	Duck seated			
299	Drake seated			
MINIATURES c1923				
800*	Pig asleep			
801	Pig asleep - larger			
802*	Two Pigs black/white	4	61	
803	Rabbit			
804	Pup playing - pale orange	S		
805	Pup playing - green/purple	S		
806*	Drake - white	2.5		1923-69
807*	Drake - green/purple	2.5		1923-77
808-815*	'Bonzo' various colourways	2	868	
818	'Ooloo' black/white	3	400	1923
819	'Ooloo' white	3	400	
820-825	Kittens - curled up -	1	898	1923-36
826*	Pekinese curled up	1		
827	Character Cat - tortoiseshell			
828	Character Cat - tabby			
829	Character Cat - black/white			
831	Seated pup			
832	Pekinese puppy - seated	2.5		
833	Pekinese puppy - standing	2		
834	Pekinese puppy - black and brown			
835	Pekinese puppy - light brown			
836	Pekinese puppy - pale brown			
837	Chow on stand - brown			
838	Chow on stand - light brown			
839	Chow on stand - white/grey			
840-45	Character Ducks			
846	Toucan			
847	Toucan - yellow			
849	Duck & ladyBirds flower centre	4.5		
850	Duck on rock			
851	Birds on tree stump			
852*	Penguin flower centre	6.5	441	
853*	Mallard Drake on rocks	3	138	
854	Budgerigar			
855	Small Birds on tree stump			

Cocker Spaniel HN1020 1187 1108 1036

Cocker and Pheasant HN1002 1028 1029 1062

Character Dogs HN982 989 944 942

Character Dogs HN924 909 923 945

HN		HT	MODEL	DATE
856	Penguin flower centre	6.5	441	1924
858	Kingfisher on rocks	3		
859	Tortoise on rocks			
860	Birds on tree stump			
861*	Polar bear - mottled blue	4.5		
862a	Kingfisher with primroses			
862b	Kingfisher with kingcups			
863-5	Ducks			
866	Fox seated			
867-74	Miniature Birdss			
875	Kingfisher on tree stump			
876	Tiger on a rock			
877	Parrot			
878	Cockerel - white	4.5		
879	Cockerel - blue/green	4.5		
880	Cockerel - yellow/green	4.5		
881*	Bulldog seated - brown/white	2.5		
882	Character Penguin - green head	7	19	
883	Two Monkeys	2.5		
884	Cockatoo - blue/orange	6.5		
885	Cockatoo - pink/purple/orange	6.5		
886	Cockatoo - red/blue/orange	6.5		
888	Cockatoo - pale blue/yellow	6.5		
889	Greyhound - black/white	5		
890	Greyhound - looking up, brown -	5	80	
891	Elephant trunk in salute	5.5		1925-43
892-7	Character Pigs in clown costume			
898*	Alsatian head	3	600	
899	Alsatian seated			
900	Fox Terrier - brown/white			
901	Fox Terrier - black/white			
902	Character Pig			
903	Character Pig			
904	Terrier puppy			
905*	Small Frog	1.5		
906	Spaniel puppy - black/white			
907	Spaniel puppy - brown/white			1926
908*	Spaniel head	3		
909*	Fox Terrier standing -	4		
910	Fox Terrier seated -			1927
911*	Tiger lying	5	533	
912*	Tiger seated head turned	7	530	
913-8	Character Toucans			
919	Leopard seated			
920*	Two Foxes - brown	3		
921	Alsatian seated	8	525	
922*	'Wilfred',	4		1928
923	Fox Terrier - standing	4		
924*	Fox Terrier - seated	6	558	
925	Two Foxes - grey/brown			
926	Two Foxes			
927*	Two Pekinese seated	3.5		
928*	Kingfisher on lustre bowl	4		
929	Terrier pup seated			
930	Alsatian pup seated			

HN		HT	MODEL	DATE
931	Terrier pup			1928
932	Scottish Terrier standing		78	
933	Scottish Terrier			
934	Scottish Terrier			
935	Pip, Squeak and Wilfred tray	4		
936	Teal			
937	Alsatian on stand			
938	Alsatian seated on stand			
939	Bear and cub - brown			
940	Bear and cub - light brown			
941	Elephant - black			
942*	Fox Terrier - brown markings	6		
943*	Fox Terrier - black/brown	5.5	16	
944*	Fox Terrier head to side	6.5		
945	Fox Terrier black/white	5.5		
946	Penguin chick			
947*	Penguin chick	8		
948	Bulldog seated brindle	6	135	
949-952*	Young elephants -		680	
953	Terrier pup - black/brown			
954	Terrier pup - black/dk brown			
955	Brown bear on all fours	5	592	
956	Mallard Drake - head up	5		
957	Spaniel - liver/white			
958	Spaniel - black/white			
960*	Character Ape & book	4		1928
961	Character Ape & book sleeping			
962	Fox Terrier head	3		
963	Fox seated	2.5		
964	Scottish Terrier - black	4		
965	Scottish Terrier - brown	4		
966	Elephant			
967	Cat seated - tabby	5	9	
968*	Pig - black/white	5	198	
969	Two Rabbits			
970*	Dachshund	4.5		
971	'Lucky' cat tray	3		
972*	Ape in dunce's cap with book	5.5		
973	Character Duck - orange	3		
974	Character Duck - lemon	3		
975*	English Setter seated, grey	6.5		1929
976	Irish Setter seated, red	6.5		
977	Duck			
978	Fox seated			
979	Hare lying, legs out	3		
980	Aberdeen Terrier - black	3.5		1930
981	Aberdeen Terrier - grey/brown	3.5		
982*	Sealyham - black patches	3		
983	Sealyham - brown patches	3		
984	Hare lying - white			
985	Hare lying - grey			
986	Alsatian seated on bowl	5		
987	Bulldog seated on bowl	4		
988	Airdale - brown	5		
989	Sealyham - brown			

Pointer HN2624

English Setter and Pheasant HN2529

Penguins
HN 134, 2633, 133
HN 104. HN 947.

HN		HT	MODEL	DATE	
990*	Tiger stalking	6		1930	
991	Tiger stalking	5.5			
992	Sealyham - black				
993	Cat asleep on cushion	3	24		
994*	Fox on pedestal	6	12		
995	Pekinese	5	166		
996	Airdale - black/blue/brown	8			
997	Terrier seated black/brown				
998	Penguin and chick				
999	Persian Cat - black/white	5	690	1930-85	

HN			HT	DATE	
1000	Cocker Spaniel CH Lucky Star of Ware - blue roan	L	6.5	1931-60	
1001	Cocker Spaniel & Pheasant liver/white	L	6.5	1931-69	
1002	Cocker Spaniel - liver/white	L	6.5	1931-60	
1003	Pekinese - dark brown				
1004	Blue Tit on bough with blossom				
1005	Thrush on bough with blossom				
1007*	Rough Haired Terrier CH Crackley Startler	L	7.5	1931-56	
1008*	Scottish Terrier - CH Albourne Arthur	L	7	1931-55	
1009	Hare and two leverets				
1010	Pekinese 'CH Bidee of Ifield' Ex	L	7	1931	
1011*	Pekinese 'CH Bidee of Ifield'	L	6.5	1931-55	
1012*	Pekinese 'CH Bidee of Ifield'	S	3	1931-85	
1013	Rough Haired Terrier CH Crackley Hunter	M	5.5	1931-60	
1014	Rough Haired Terrier CH Crackley Hunter	S	4	1931-85	
1015	Scottish Terrier CH Albourne Arthur	M	5	1931-60	
1016	Scottish Terrier CH Albourne Arthur	S	3.5	1931-85	
1017	Scottish Terrier seated	L	7	1931	
1018*	Scottish Terrier seated	M	5	1931	
1019	Scottish Terrier seated	S	3.5	1931 (333)	
1020*	Cocker Spaniel CH Lucky Star of Ware blue roan	M	5	1985	
1021	Cocker Spaniel CH Lucky Star of Ware blue roan		S	4	1931-69
1022*	Airdale CH Cotsford Topsail	L	8	1931-60	
1023	Airdale CH Cotsford Topsail	M	5	1931-85	
1024	Airdale CH Cotsford Topsail	S	4	1931-69	
1025*	Foxhound CH Tring Rattler	L	8	1931-55	
1026	Foxhound CH Tring Rattler	M	5	1931-60	
1027	Foxhound CH Tring Rattler	S	4	1931-1956	
1028*	Cocker and Pheasant liver/white	M	5	1931-85	
1029*	Cocker and Pheasant liver/white	S	4	1931-69	
1030*	Sealyham CH Scotia Stylist	L	5	1931-55	
1031	Sealyham CH Scotia Stylist	M	4	1931-55	
1032	Sealyham CH Scotia Stylist	S	3	1931-1960	
1033*	Cairn CH Charming Eyes grey	L	7	1931-55	
1034	Cairn CH Charming Eyes grey	M	4.5	1931-1960	
1035	Cairn CH Charming Eyes grey	S	3	1931-85	
1036	Cocker Spaniel liver/white	M	5	1931-85	
1037*	Cocker Spaniel liver/white	S	3.5	1931-69	
1038	Scottish Terrier begging			1931	
1039	Pekinese seated	L	7	1931	
1040*	Pekinese seated	S	3	1928-43	
1041	Sealyham lying	L		1931	
1042	Bulldog - brindle	L	6	1931-60	
1043	Bulldog - brindle	M	5	1931-60	
1044*	Bulldog - brindle	S	3	1931-69	

HN			HT	DATE
1045	Bulldog - brown/white	L	6	1931-60
1046	Bulldog - brown/white	M	5	1931-60
1047	Bulldog - brown/white	S	3	1931-85
1048	West Highland Terrier	L	7	1931
1049	English Setter *CH Maesydd Mustard*	L	8	1931-60
1050*	English Setter *CH Maesydd Mustard*	M	5	1931-85
1051	English Setter *CH Maesydd Mustard*	S	4	1931-69
1052	Sealyham lying	M		1931-
1053	Sealyham lying	S		1931-
1054*	Irish Setter *CH Pat O'Moy* Red	L	8	1931-60
1055	Irish Setter *CH Pat O'Moy*	M	5	1931-85
1056	Irish Setter *CH Pat O'Moy*	S	4	1931-69
1057	Collie *CH Ashstead Applause*	L	7.5	1931-60
1058	Collie *CH Ashstead Applause*	M	5	1931-85
1059*	Collie *CH Ashstead Applause*	S	4	1931-69
1062*	Cocker and Pheasant black/white	S	4	1931-69
1063*	Cocker and Hare liver/white	M	5	1931-35
1064	Cocker and Hare liver/white	S	4	1931-35
1065*	Greyhound - brindle	L	8.5	1931-55
1066	Greyhound - brindle	M	6	1931-55
1067	Greyhound - brindle	S	5	1931-60
1068*	Smth Hrd Terrier *CH Chosen Don of Notts*	L	8.5	1931
1069	Smth Hrd Terrier *CH Chosen Don of Notts*	M	6	1931-60
1070	Smth Hrd Terrier *CH Chosen Don of Notts*	S	5	1931
1071	Hare lying			1931
1072	Bulldog - white	L	6	1931-60
1073	Bulldog - white	M	5	1931-60
1074	Bulldog - white	S	3	1931-85
1075	Greyhound black/white	L	8.5	1931-56
1076*	Greyhound black/white	M	6	1931-55
1077	Greyhound black/white	S	5	1931-55
1078	Cocker Spaniel black/white	S	3	1931-69
1079*	Gordon Setter - black/tan	L	8	1931-55
1080	Gordon Setter - black/tan	M	5	1931-55
1081	Gordon Setter - black/tan	S	4	1931-60
1082*	Tiger stalking	L	4.5	1931
1083	Tiger stalking	M	3	1931
1084	Tiger stalking	S	2	1931
1085	Lion	L	6.5	1931
1086*	Lion	M	5	1931

ASHTRAYS* 3" model 154-155 1933-
1087-1093 Robin, Mouse, Squirrel, Rabbit, and Wren (1089)

1094	Leopard			1934-
1095	Ashtray		3	1934-
1095a	Ashtray		3	1934-
1096	Character Fox with goose			1934-

DOGS OF CHARACTER*

1097	-Running with ball		2	1934-85
1098	-Lying on back		2	1934-59
1099	-Yawning		4	1934-85
1100	-Bull Terrier walking		4	1934-59
1101	-Lying yawning		2	1934-59
1102	Character Fox with goose			1934
1103*	Character dog with ball		2.75	1934-86
1104	Cairn - black	L	7	1937

Fox
HN 147

Cockerals
HN 184
HN 124
HN 157

Foxes. 4 positions in 3 sizes HN 149

HN 2634

HN 130

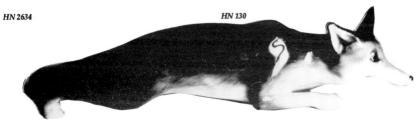

HN			HT	DATE	
1105	Cairn - black	M	4.5	1937	
1106	Cairn - black	S	3	1937	
1107	Cairn - black	L	7.5	1937	
1108*	Cocker Spaniel - black/white	M	6.5	1937-60	
1109*	Cocker Spaniel - black/white	S	5	1937-85	
1111*	Dalmatian *CH Goworth Victor*	L	8.5	1937-55	
1112	Lion	L		1937	
1113	Dalmatian *CH Goworth Victor*	M	5.5	1937-85	
1114	Dalmatian *CH Goworth Victor*	S	4	1937-69	
1115*	Alsatian *CH Benign of Picardy*	L	9	1937-60	
1116	Alsatian *CH Benign of Picardy*	M	6	1937-85	
1117	Alsatian *CH Benign of Picardy*	S	4	1937-69	
1118	Tiger on rock	L	12	1937	
1119	Lion on rock	L	11	1937	
1120	Fighting Elephant matt grey	L	24L	1937 (626)	
1121*	Elephant	L	13	1937-60	
1122	Elephant	L	13	1937	
1123	Elephant	M		1937	
1124	Elephant	L	13	1937	
1125	Lion on alabaster base			1937	
1126*	Tiger on alabaster base		4	1937	
1127*	Dachshund *CH Shrewd Saint* black	L	6	1937-55	
1128	Dachshund *CH Shrewd Saint* black	M	4	1937-85	
1129	Dachshund *CH Shrewd Saint* black	S	3	1937-69	
1130*	Fox by Raoh Schorr		11	1937 (678)	
1131	Staffordshire Bull Terrier	L	9	1937	
1132	Staffordshire Bull Terrier	M	6.5	1937-60	
1133	Staffordshire Bull Terrier	S	4.5	1937	
1134	Cocker Spaniel - liver/white	L	6.5	1937	
1135	Cocker Spaniel - liver/white	M	5	1937	
1136*	Cocker Spaniel - liver/white	S	3	1937	
1137	Cocker and Pheasant - black/white	L	6.5	1937	
1138	Cocker and Pheasant - black/white	M	5	1937	
1139*	Dachshund - brown	L	6	1937-55	
1140	Dachshund - brown	M	4	1937-69	
1141	Dachshund - brown	S	3	1937-69	
1142*	Bull Terrier *CH Bokus Brock*	L	9	1937	
1143	Bull Terrier *CH Bokus Brock*	M	6.5	1937	
1144	Bull Terrier *CH Bokus Brock*	S	4.5	1937	
RAOH SCHORR - Green Bronze			HT	MODEL	DATE
1145	Moufflon standing -		6	952	1937-42
1146*	Calf sleeping		2	946	1937-42
1147	Calf standing		6	947	
1148*	Buffalo		7	948	
1149	Donkey - head back		6	949	
1150	Young Doe		4.5	950	
1151	Swiss Goat		5	951	
1152	Horse		6	953	
1153	Moufflon lying		2	954	
1154	Jumping Goat		7	955	
1155	Donkey - head forward		6	956	
1156	Suspicious Doe		6	957	
1157	Antelope		6	958	
1158*	Character dog with plate		3.5		1937-85
1159*	Character dog with bone		3.5		1937-85

HN			HT	MODEL	DATE
RAOH SCHORR - Cream Matt					
1160	Moufflon standing -		6	952	1937-42
1161	Calf - sleeping		2	946	
1162	Calf - standing		6	947	
1163	Buffalo		7	948	
1164	Donkey - head back		6	949	
1165	Young Doe		4.5	950	
1166	Swiss goat		5	951	
1167	Horse		6	953	
1168	Moufflon lying		2	954	
1169	Jumping Goat		7	955	
1170	Donkey - head forward		6	956	
1171	Suspicious Doe		6	957	
1172	Antelope		6	958	
RAOH SCHORR - Natural Colours					
1173	Calf sleeping -		2	946	1937-42
1174	Calf standing		6	947	
1175	Buffalo		7	948	
1176	Donkey - head back		6	949	
1177	Young Doe		4.5	950	
1178	Swiss Goat		5	951	
1179	Moufflon standing		6	952	
1180	Horse		6	953	
1181	Moufflon lying		2	954	
1182*	Jumping Goat		7	955	
1183	Donkey - head forward		6	956	
1184	Suspicious Doe		6	957	
1185	Antelope		6	958	
1186*	Cocker Spaniel - liver	L	6.5		1937-60
1187*	Cocker Spaniel - liver	M	5		1937-85
1188	Cocker Spaniel - liver	S	3		1937-69
1189	Penguin		7.5		1937
1190	Peruvian Penguin short beak		8	21	1936
1191	Drake - sitting up		5.5		
1192	Duck seated		3.5		
1193	Tern male		2.5		
1194	Tern female		2.5		
1195	Blackheaded Gull - male		4		
1196	Blackheaded Gull - female		4		
1197	Gannet shaded in lemon/grey		7	243	
1198	Drake				
1199	Penguin - short beak	L	7		1938
RAOH SCHORR -					1939-42
2500	Cerval- white matt		8		
2501	Lynx - white matt		3.5		
2502	Seated Deer - green matt		2		
2503	Seated Deer - white matt		2		
2504	Sleeping Lamb - green matt		2		
2505	Sleeping Lamb - white matt		2		
2506	Asiatic Elephant - green matt				
2507	Wildebeest - green matt				
DOGS OF CHARACTER 1938-59					
2508*	Sealyham head turned		3		
2509	Sealyham standing		2.5		
2510	Dog running		3		

Puppies
HN 194
HN 128
HN 166

Tern
HN 168

Pig HN 965
Monkey HN 183
Early Pelican
Dachshund HN 970

Courtesy Gossland

HN			HT	DATE	MODEL
2511	Bull Terrier barking		4	1938-59	
2512*	Smth Hrd Terrier *CH Chosen Don of Notts*	L	8.5	1938	
2513	Smth Hrd Terrier *CH Chosen Don of Notts*	M	6	1938-60	
2514	Smth Hrd Terrier *CH Chosen Don of Notts*	S	4.5	1938	
2515	Springer Spaniel *CH Dry Toast*	L	8	1938-55	
2516	Springer Spaniel *CH Dry Toast*	M	5	1938-67	
2517*	Springer Spaniel *CH Dry Toast*	S	4	1938-85	
2518	*Pride of the Shires* mare with brown foal	L	9	1938	
2519	*The Gude Grey Mare* with foal	L	7	1938-60	1910
2520	*The Farmers Boy* dappled Shire and rider	L	9	1938-60	
2521	*The Dapple Grey* pony and rider	L	7	1938	
2522	*The Chestnut Mare* with foal	L	6.5	1938-60	1020
2523	*Pride of the Shires* grey mare and foal	L	9	1938-60	1018
2524*	American Foxhound	L	8	1938-55	
2525	American Foxhound	M	5	1938-60	
2526	American Foxhound	S	4	1938	
2527	Fox seated		10.5	1938	
2528	*Pride of the Shires* - Brown	L	9	1938-60	1018
2529*	English Setter and Pheasant	L	8	1938-85	
2530	*Merely a Minor* Brown Hunter	l	12	1938-60	
2531*	*Merely a Minor* - Grey Hunter	L	12	1938-60	
2532*	*The Gude Grey Mare* with foal	M	5.5	1940-67	1910a
2533*	*The Chestnut Mare* with foal	S	5	1940-60	1020b
2534	*Pride of the Shires* brown foal	M	6.5	1940-60	1018a
2535	Tiger on a rock		4.5	1940-60	
2536	*Pride of the Shires*	S	4.5	1940-60	1018
2537*	*Merely a Minor* Bay - white stockings	M	9.5	1940-60	
2538	*Merely a Minor* Grey	M	9.5	1940-60	
2539	Persian Cat white		5	1940-76	690
2540	Kingfisher on tree stump flying down		4.5	1940	258
2541	Kingfisher on tree stump flying down		3.5	1940	258a
2542	Baltimore Oriole		4	1940	
2543*	Blue Birds with mauve lupins		6		
2544	Mallard Drake with spill vase		8		
2545	Cock Pheasant on base		7		
2546	Yellow Throated Warbler floral		4.5		
2547*	Two Budgerigars on tree stump		6		
2548	Golden Crested Wren on prunus		4.5		
2549	English Robin with floral base		2.5		
2550	Chaffinch on branch		2.5		
2551	Bullfinch		5.5		
2552*	Two *Young Thrushes*		3	1938	1071
2553	Two *Young Robins* on branch		3	1939	
2554	Cardinal on tree stump		5	1940	
2555	Mallard Duck head out		6		
2556*	Mallard Duck head out		4		
2557*	Welsh Corgi *CH Spring Robin*	L	8	1940-55	
2558	Welsh Corgi *CH Spring Robin*	M	5	1940	
2559	Welsh Corgi *CH Spring Robin*	S	4	1940	
2560	Great Dane L		8.5	1940	
2561*	Great Dane M		6	1940-60	
2562	Great Dane S		4.5	1940	
2563	*Pride of the Shires*	L	9	1940	1073
2564*	*Pride of the Shires*	M	6.5	1940	1073a
2565	*The Chestnut Mare*	L	6.5	1940	1074

HN			HT	DATE	MODEL
2566	*The Chestnut Mare*	S	5	1940	1074a
2567	*Merely a Minor*	S	6	1940	
2568	*The Gude Grey Mare*	L	7	1940	
2569	*The Gude Grey Mare*	M	5.5	1940	
2570	*The Gude Grey Mare*	S	4	1940	
2571	*Merely a Minor*	S	6	1940	1039b
2572*	Mallard Duck - head up		2		
2573*	Kingfisher		2.5		
2574*	Herring Gull on rock		2	1940	
2575	Swan		2		15
2576	Pheasant as miniature 2545		2	1942	
2577	Peacock on grass base		2.5		
2578	Horse - *Dapple grey* without rider		7	1942-60	2520

CHARACTER KITTENS* 1941-85

HN		HT	DATE	MODEL
2579	Lying on back	1.5		
2580	Licking back paw	2		
2581	Sleeping	1.5		
2582	On hind legs	3		
2583	Licking front paw	2		1162
2584	Looking up	2		1165

CHARACTER PUPPIES* 1941-85

2585	Spaniel in basket liver/white -		2		1155
2586	Cocker Spaniel Black/White				
2587	Terrier in basket		3		
2588	3 Terriers in basket		3		
2589	Cairn begging		4		
2590	2 Spaniels sleeping		2	1941-69	
2591*	Drake med. green head		2.5	1941-69	
2592*	Hare with ears errect		3	1941-69	1157
2593	Hare with legs behind	L	7L	1941-69	656
2594	Hare with legs behind	S	2	1941-85	656a
2595-2598	Lambs				
2599*	English Setter and Pheasant		8.5		
2600	Cocker Spaniel and Pheasant black		4		
2601*	American Great Dane	L	8.5	1941-55	
2601	American Great Dane	M	6.5	1941-60	
2603	American Great Dane	S	4.5		

ENGLISH BUTTERFLIES   Florals 1941   MODEL

2604	Peacock	2	1178
2605	Camberwell Beauty	2	1176
2606*	Swallow Tail	2	1175
2607	Red Admiral	2	1179
2608	Copper	2	1177
2609	Tortoiseshell	2	1180
2610*	Hen Pheasant	6	1195
2611	Chaffinch	2	
2612	Baltimore Oriel	4	
2613*	Golden Crested Wren	4.5	
2614	Blue Birds	5	
2615	Cardinal	4.5	
2616	Bullfinch	4	
2617	Robin	2	
2618	Yellow Throated Warbler	4.5	
2619	Grouse		

Rhino
HN 141

Polar Bear
HN 861

Tiger
HN 225

Hare
HN 2592

Budgies
HN 2547

St Beranard
HN 231

Hare
HN 2594

HN			HT	MODEL	DATE
2620	English Setter - liver & white	L	7.5		1950
2621	English Setter M		5		
2622	English Setter S		4		
2623*	*Punch Peon* chestnut Shire		7.5		1950-1134
2624*	Pointer on base		5		1952-85
2625	Poodle not issued	L			
2626	Poodle not issued	M			
2627	Poodle not issued	S			
2628	Chow not issued	L			
2629	Chow not issued	M			
2630	Chow not issued	S			
2631*	French poodle	M	5		1952-85
2632*	Cock Pheasant		7		1952-79
2633*	Penguin - Peruvian	L	13		1952-73
2634*	Fox seated		10.5		1952-C
2635	Drake white	L	13.5		1952-73
2636	Indian Runner Drake	L	7.5		
2637	Polar bear & cub on green base		15		
2638	Leopard on rock		9		1952-C
2639	Tiger on rock		11.5		1952-C
2640	Fighter Elephant		11.5		1952-C
2641	Lion on rock		10.5		1952-C
2642	Red Squirrel in a pine tree		8L		
2643*	Boxer *CH Warlord of Mazelaine*	M	6		1952-85
2644*	Elephant with trunk in salute	S	5.5	489	1952-85
2645*	Dobermann *CH Rancho Dobe's Storm* M		6		1955-85
2646	Tiger stalking		6	809	1959-C
2647	Drake				

*CHARACTER PIGLETS 1959-67

HN		HT	MODEL	DATE
2648	Squatting	2		
2649	Standing	2		
2650	Lying	1	1282	
2651	Sleeping	1	1280	
2652	Sitting	2	1281	
2653	Rooting	2		
2654	Character dog with slipper	3		1959-85

CHATCULL RANGE*

HN		HT	DATE
2655	Siamese Cat seated	5	1960-85
2656	Pine Martin	4	1960-69
2657	Langur Monkey	4.5	1960-69
2658	White Tailed Deer	6	1960-69
2659	Brown Bear	4	1960-69
2660	Siamese Cat standing	5	1960-85
2661	Mountain Sheep standing	5	1960-69
2662	Siamese Cat lying	4	1960-85
2663	River Hog	3.5	1960-69
2664	Nyala Antelope		1960-69
2665	Llama		1960-69
2666	Badger		1960-69
2667*	Labrador *CH Bumblekite of Mansergh* M	5	1967-85

JEFFERSON SCULPTURES

HN		HT	DATE
2668	Puffins	11	1974
2669	Snowy Owl male 16		1974
2670	Snowy Owl female	9.5	1974
3500	Black-Throated Loon	11	1974

HN		HT	DATE	
3501	White Winged Cross Bills	8	1974	
3502	King Eider	11	1974	
3503	Roseate Turns	12	1974	
3504*	Golden Crowned Kinglet	8	1974	
3505	Winter Wren	5	1974	
3506	Colorado Chipmunks	13	1974	
3507	Harbour Seals	8.5	1975	
3508	Snowshoe Hares	713	1975	
3509*	Downy Woodpecker	8	1975	
3510	Fledgling Blue Birds	6	1976	
3511	Chipping Sparrow	7.5	1976	

LEM WARD 4" 1979-85

HN		HT	DATE	
3512	Mallard - male			
3513	Pintail - male			
3514*	Greater Scaup - male			
3515	Mallard - female			
3516	Pintail - female			
3517*	Greater Scaup - female			
3518	Merganser - male		1980-85	
3519	Merganser - female		1980-85	
3520	Green wing tail - male		1981-85	
3521	Green wing tail female		1981-85	

IMAGES OF NATURE

HN		HT	DATE	
3522	*The Leap* - Dolphin	9	1982-C	
3523	*Capricorn* - mountain Goat	10	1982-C	
3524	*The Gift of Life* - mare & foal	9	1982-C	
3525	*Courtship* - Terns	15	1982-C	
3526	*Shadow Pay* - Cat	10	1982-C	
3527	*Going Home* - Geese	6	1982-C	
3528	*Freedom* - Otter	8.5	1983-6	
3529	*Bright Water* - Two Otters	8.5	1983-6	
3530	*Clear Water* - Otter	8.5	1983-6	
3531	*Nestling Down* - Swans	13	1986-C	
3532	*The Homecoming* - Doves	15	1987-C	
3533	*Patience* - Heron	12	1987-C	
3534	*Playful* - Lion Cubs	7.5	1987-C	
3535	*Courtship* - Terns	15	1987-C	flambé
3536	*The Gift of Life* - Mare & foal	9	1987-C	flambé
3537	*Nestling Down* - Swans	13	1987-C	flambé
3539	*The Homecomming* - Doves	15	1990-C	flambé
3540	*Graceful* - two Panthers	11L	1989-C	
3542	*Serenity* - Shoal of Fish	11	1990-C	
3543	Friendship - Dog & Cat	8	1990-C	
3547	Pegasus (Alan Malankowski)	11	1990-C	

UNCLASSIFIED AND NEW FINDS

HN		HT	DATE
6448*	*Huntsman Fox* standing	4.5	-85
	Monkey in armchair (437)	4	c1926
*	Pelican beak down	6.5	c1910
	Polar Bear on hind legs green base	10	
	Lyre Bird Aus. Bi-Cent. Jo Ledger	30	1988 (6 made)

N.B.   HN 2636 & 2642 are by Peggy Davies

Parakeet, Cardinal, 2 Great Tits, Chaffinch as HN2550

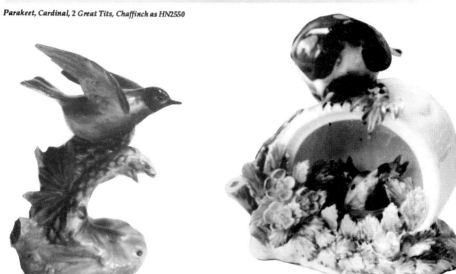

American Bluebird HN2543 6"

Bird and nest 3"

There are many birds throughout the list which have elaborate floral settings. First appearing in 1940. The floral nest in a crock was available in 1977. The group at the top are c.1980. Some later adaptations can be found with Royal Adderley backstamps.

COLLECTORS NOTES -

In the listings measurements are in inches and refer to height unless otherwise
stated i.e. L = Length.   Measurements are to the nearest quarter inch.
Illustrated pieces are marked with an asterisk.
Prices in old shillings are aproximately:- 20/- = UK £1 = U.S. $1.60 = Aus. $2.
HN - named for Harry Nixon. Head of Painting Dept in 1913.
DA - Doulton Animal - new prefix introduced in 1989.
H- Leslie Harradine's Lambeth slip cast pieces have an H catalogue prefix.
Model numbers indicate when the design was *first* issued.

100 -153	...... 1913 - 1915	2500 - 2670	..... 1938 - 1974
154 - 299	..... 1918 - 1930	3500 - 3519	..... 1974 - 1980
800 - 1200	.... 1923 - 1936	3522 - 3542	..... 1982 - 1990

A design book specifically staes that HN255 was issued 18 / 7 / 1921
The HN numbers do not always run in issue date sequence i.e. there is a sec-
tion for miniatures from HN 800 - . As the bases of these were too small to
accomodate dates I have not been able to record many of these.
Some HN numbers are ascribed to different models and colourways principally
HN 145 Fledgling birds. HN 147 Foxes which includes four poses in three sizes.
From HN 2502 animal and figurine numbers can coincide.
With dates I have made what I hope are intelligent guesses in some instances.
Dates of issue and discontinuation have to be viewed with flexibility. A lot of
my dates come from the U.S.A. where the range discontinued there in 1984 were
still available in the shops in the UK in 1986 so that I have compromised with
a 1985 date. The time lag for the introduction of new issues can be as much as
two years in Australia.
Many animal models were discontinued in WWII never to be reinstated and
most others in 1985 (1984 in U.S.A.).   C = In current production.
The *Championship* name printed on the animals foot was discontinued at some
stage. Perhaps as the significance of the name faded but more probably to save
cost. The Dobermann *Rancho Dobe's Storm* HN 2645 1955 bears the label.
Painters marks are numerous and varied.
The earlier Animal models can occur in many glazes other than the regular one.
They appear in the Doulton *Flambé, Sung, Chang, Titanian, Chinese Jade, Kingsware, Treacle, Bronze, Lustre* and in plain matt glazes. There are too many to list
but don't be surprised at anything you find.
Some models are shown in a *flambé* glaze if a photograph of the regular colouring was not available.
Reference is made to models in *Doulton Flambé Animals* by J Lukins 1981.
Many bird and animal models were produced principally for the North American market and are indigenous to that continent. I have not explained species
but you can have great fun looking them up. e.g. *Moufflon* is an agile Sicilian
sheep.

CHAMPIONSHIP DOGS (and a few strays)   *Catalogue 1933*
by Ann Cook and Jocelyn Lukins.

The most collected animal group of all are the faithfully modelled reproductions of recognised dog breeds and show ring champions. The first one modelled from life by Frederick Daws was issued in 1931. *Lucky Star of Ware* HN 1000 was Crufts Champion 'Best in Show' in 1930 and 1931. The dog was a blue roan owned by Mr H.S. Lloyd whose cocker spaniels were 'Best in Show' also in 1938, 1939, 1948 and 1950 which in fact were successive shows as these were the difficult days of the second world war and after. This record has never been beaten by any other breed. The cocker was very popular at this time and *Lucky Star of Ware* was the epitome of his type. He was very finely modelled by Frederick Daws who modelled all the champions for the next twenty years. From quite early in production the faithfully executed blue roan colouring was changed to plain black as it was obviously so much easier to produce. This may account for the name change to '*Lucky Pride of Ware*'. Catalogues still specify *Lucky Star of Ware* until quite late but printers copy doesn't always note such changes.

The Cocker Spaniel and his sporting cousin the Springer account for quite a large number of models in the HN list. Even the Lambeth factory produced one sleepy spaniel model by Leslie Harradine. The standing Championship *Cocker Spaniel* was produced in four colours; blue roan or black, liver, black and white and liver and white. Seated and carrying a pheasant it came in three sizes and two colourings, black and white and liver and white.

Cocker and Pheasant HN 1028 Irish Setter HN 1054 Cocker Spaniel HN 1108

Carrying a hare in its mouth it was made in liver and white and only two sizes, medium and small. These last two models were not popular and are rare today. The Springer Spaniel should have been the dog chosen to be shown with the game as it is more often used as a gun dog. It was only produced in the standing position with head just slightly turned and came in the three sizes and one colourway dark brown and white. The Springer Spaniel is considered by experts to be one of the best sculpted dogs in the series and holding up well to its present day standard for the breed. Including the early spaniels HN 906/7 and HN 957/8, all the Championship models, the mounted heads, six brooches, the later four character dogs and the miniature K 9. There are almost fifty different spaniels to collect.

Springer Spaniel Hn 2517

SPANIEL DIGEST

HN	TITLE	COLOUR		HT	DATES
906	Spaniel pup	black & white			
907	Spaniel pup	brown & white			
908	Spaniel's head	blue roan	L	3	
908	Spaniel's head	liver & white	L	3	
908	Spaniel's head		L	3	
957	Spaniel	liver & white	M	2.5	
958	Spaniel	black & white	M	2.5	
1000	LUCKY STAR OF WARE	blue roan or black	L	6.5	1931-1960
1001	COCKER & PHEASANT	liver & white	L	6.5	-1969
1002	LUCKY STAR OF WARE	liver & white	L	6.5	-1960
1020	LUCKY STAR OF WARE	blue roan or black	M	5	-1985
1021	LUCKY STAR OF WARE	blue roan or black	S	4	-1969
1028	COCKER & PHEASANT	liver & white	M	5	-1985
1029	COCKER & PHEASANT	liver & white	S	4	-1969
1036	LUCKY PRIDE OF WARE	liver & white	M	5	-1985
1037	LUCKY PRIDE OF WARE	liver & white	S	3.5	-1969
1062	COCKER & PHEASANT	black & white	S	4	-1969
1063	COCKER & HARE	liver & white	M	5	1931-
1064	COCKER & HARE	liver & white		3	1931-
1078	LUCKY PRIDE OF WARE	black & white	S	3	1938 -1969
1108	LUCKY PRIDE OF WARE	black & white	L	6.5	1938 -1960
1109	LUCKY PRIDE OF WARE	black & white	M	5	1938 -1985
1134	LUCKY PRIDE OF WARE	liver & white	L	6.5	1938
1135	LUCKY PRIDE OF WARE	liver & white	M	5	1938
1136	LUCKY PRIDE OF WARE	liver & white	S	3	1938
1137	COCKER & PHEASANT	black & white	L	6.5	
1138	COCKER & PHEASANT	black & white	M	5	
1186	LUCKY PRIDE OF WARE	liver	L	6.5	
1187	LUCKY PRIDE OF WARE	liver	M	5	
1188	LUCKY PRIDE OF WARE	liver	S	3.5	
2515	DRY TOAST Springer	brown & white	L	6.5	1938 -1955
2516	DRY TOAST	brown & white	M	5	1938 -1967
2517	DRY TOAST	brown & white	S	4	1938 -1985
2585	Cocker in basket	liver & white		3	1941 -1985
2586	Cocker in basket	black & white		3	1941 -1985
2590	2 Cockers sleeping	1 liver & 1 black		2	1941 -1985
2600	Cocker & pheasant	black	S	4	1941 -
K 9	Bandaged paw	liver		2	1931 -1977
	Brooch	blue roan	LMS	-2	1933
	Brooch	liver & white	LMS	-2	1933

The second breed introduced into the range was also a very popular dog in the 1930's. The wire haired fox terrier with his characteristic clean cut trim is represented by *CH Crackley Startler* HN 1007, later re-named *Crackley Hunter*. Perhaps the owner of *Crackley Startler* disapproved of the model and the name had to be changed? He was followed by *CH Albourne Arthur* HN 1008 another very fashionable dog of the day. Either of these dogs was an almost obligatory ladies fashion accessory much as the Poodle was in the 1950's. The Fox Terrier and the Scottie occur in various versions early in the list and the Scottie occurs seated in three sizes HN 1017/8/9 and begging HN 1038 with two K models.

Fox Terrier HN 1007

Scottish Terrier HN 1008

Bull Terrier HN 1143

Cairn HN 1033

Seated Scottie HN 1019

There are altogether fifteen different Scotties to collect in the championship stance. Both terriers occur in the usual three sizes. All true terriers originate in the British Isles and Royal Doulton was ready to capitalize on these home-grown breeds. The Bull Terrier, now one of the most collectable breeds is represented by CH Bokus Brock. The same mould was also used to produce a *Staffordshire* terrier which to the modern day fancier 'Staffordshire' is not accurate as that breed has changed considerably and indeed, probably never looked much like this figure.

Cairn HN 1033 Sealyham HN 1031 Scottish Terrier HN 1008

Royal Doulton produced a great number of Cairn terriers in different colours and bodies. The champion represented was called *Charming eyes*. A further Cairn is found begging HN 2589 in the character dog series and K 11 is a seated Cairn. The Cairn was more popular in England than in the United States, in spite of the fact that Dorothy's 'Toto' in *The Wizard of Oz* 1939 was a cairn. Doulton used this same mould to produce a rare West Highland Terrier HN 1048 in white and in the large size only although un-numbered white pieces have been found in other sizes. Oddly enough, the present-day Westie is far better represented by this mould than is the contemporary Cairn. A Westie, *Olac Moon Pilot*, was *Crufts* 'Best in Show' for 1990. A very sharp little fellow with a tail 'like a Christmas tree'. He won the hearts of the T.V. millions as well as the approval of the judge.

Airdale HN 1022

Smooth Haired Terrier HN 1069

The Smooth Haired Terrier *Chosen Don of Notts* was made in three sizes, all of which are difficult to find. Rarity is always due to the breed not being so popular and the model therefore selling in smaller numbers.

Smooth Haired Terrier HN 2512 rarer colourway

The Airdale known as 'the King of terriers' is represented by *CH Cotsford Topsail* in the usual three sizes and a rather rare K 5 represents an Airdale lying down.

Another terrier popular in the 1930's was the Sealyham, originating in Wales. In addition to the three sizes of *CH Scotia Stylist* in the show pose, the Sealyham was also made in three sizes in a lying position HN 1041,1052/3. Earlier models were made with different ear and head markings. There is a fine sealyham looking back HN 2508 and standing HN 2509 in the character series and two different positions in the K series. Sealyhams are noted for their 'sit-up' capabilities and the artist captured this rascal with all his charm in the K 3. The Sealyham began to lose its popularity in the United States when it was replaced by the appeal of the movie star Wire Haired Fox Terrier, 'Asta', who appeared in the 'Thin Man' series 1934-44 and President Rosevelt's favorite a Scottie called 'Fala'.

Sealyham HN 1030

English Setter HN 1050

Irish Setter Hn 1054

Gordon Setter HN 1074

The Setters also came from Britain, the black and tan Gordon Setter is native to Scotland, as the Red Setter is to Ireland and the English Setter *CH Maesydd Mustard* was the model for all three breeds. The English Setter is in black and white in three sizes, the liver and white version is extremely rare. The Gordon Setter, black and tan, is quite rare in all three sizes. The English Setter retrieving a pheasant HN 2529 and the Pointer HN 2624 'on point' are two sporting dogs modelled in action poses and introduced as late as 1952 in an impressive large size only. The Setter was modelled as all previous dogs by Frederick Dawes but the Pointer was modelled by Peggy Davies.

Collie HN 1057
Alsatian HN 1115

The Collie which originated in Scotland was expert at handling large flocks of sheep. He is represented by *CH Ashstead Applause*. It was made in the usual three sizes but there is an early seated model HN 105 issued in 1913 which was made in quite large numbers. Another working dog, the Alsatian, *CH Benign of Picardy* was issued in three sizes and like the Collie occurs in a fine seated model HN 921 and a miniature seated K 13. The original name of German Shepherd, changed in a patriotic fervour during world war one has now been restored to the breed. Many of these dogs act as serving members of the British Army for ceremonial and guard dog duties.

Greyhound HN 1065   Greyhound HN 1076

The Greyhound, modelled in three sizes and two colourways, was not allotted a champions name. It occurs in an early seated version too. 'A night at the dogs' at the local greyhound stadium is a more popular pastime in Britain and Australia than in the USA where it was invented in 1919. Of the breeds of Foxhound in the Championship series, the English *CH Tring Ratler* and the American, the latter has noticably larger ears. Both have prominent tails but not as much as that of the Dalmatian *CH Goworth Victor* which was made in three sizes and it is unusual to find one with a perfect tail as they are so vulnerable.

Dalmatian HN 1111 Great Dane HN 2561 Bulldog HN 1047 Alsatian HN 1117

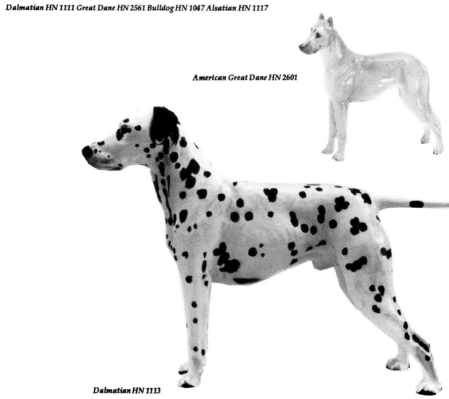

American Great Dane HN 2601

Dalmatian HN 1113

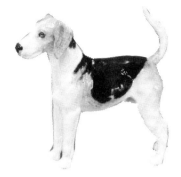

Welsh Corgi HN 2558   *American Foxhound HN 2524*

One of the best dogs created by Royal Doulton is the Welsh Corgi *CH Spring Robin* issued in three sizes in 1940. A favorite dog of the Royal family, the foxy face and rich red coat of this breed makes it a delightful sculpture. The great Dane *CH Rebeller of Ouborough* and it's American counterpart are the only female models of any breed in the Championship series. The American Great Dane and the English Great Dane differ only in the ears, which are left natural and uncropped in Great Britain.

English Foxhound HN 1025

Pekinese HN 1040

The Pekinese centuries ago was a great favorite at the Chinese Imperial court and it was not until the sacking of the Summer Palace, Peking in 1860 by the French and English that they came to Europe where they established themselves as great favorites too. This is a breed which is very much collected so that I thought a list would be helpful.

The Pekinese *CH Bidee of Ifield* HN 1010 was the only dog which was made in an extra large size. A large and small size completed the trio. The two puppies HN 832 and HN 833 have been found with a *Chinese jade* glaze very suitable to the subject and all these small pekes can be found mounted in various ways as ashtrays and paperweights. There is even a small curled peke forming the centre of an ashtray HN 826.

PEKINESE DIGEST

HN	DESCRIPTION		HT	DATE
127	Peke looking up		3.5	1920
826	Curled Peke ashtray		-1	1923
832	Puppy sitting		2.5	1931
833	Puppy standing		2	1931
834	Puppy standing black/brown		2.5	1931
835	Puppy standing golden brown		2.5	1931
836	Puppy standing sand		2.5	1931
927	Two Pekes		3.5	1931
995	Pekinese		5	1931
1003	Pekinese dk. colour		5	1931
1010	*CH Bidee of Ifield*	EX/L	7	1931
1011	*CH Bidee of Ifield*	L	5.5	1931
1012	*CH Bidee of Ifield*	S	3	1931
1039	Peke seated	L	5.5	1931
1040	Peke seated	S	3	1931
	Head Mask		3.5	1933
K 6	miniature		2	1931
(371)	Ervan Lucas Bols flask		6	1940

Bulldogs HN 1044 HN 1074 HN 1047

The Bulldog was originally kept for bull baiting abolished in England in 1838 but it has since been bred into a much gentler creature. It became the symbol of Britain at war, 'The Bulldog Breed', and in both world wars Doulton created patriotic Bulldog models. In 1917 they produced the large khaki seated Bulldogs in tin hat, tammy and haversacks representing English and Scottish soldiers and in 1941 they came out with a series of the seated bulldog with added Union Jacks. Two other models were given head gear and cigars as a charicature of Winston Churchill, the wartime leader. Earlier in 1919 and 1932 the same seated Bulldog with Union Jacks was used for the advertising pieces. One model of a large size seated Bulldog exists in khaki glaze and added Union Jack and another with an eye patch. Other unusual unlisted versions of the Bulldog have been found with even some fakes. The Bulldog is the most collected of all Doulton models and there is a wide diversity of pieces to collect.

Khaki Glaze Bulldogs HN 153 HN 146

BULLDOG DIGEST

HN		HT	DATE
129	Seated Bulldog	6	1917
146	Khaki glaze and tin hat	6.5	1918
153	Khaki glaze and tammy	7	1918
881	Seated Bulldog	2.5	1926
948	Seated Bulldog brindle	6	1929
987	Seated Bulldog on bowl	3.5	1929
1042	Bulldog - brindle	6	1931
1042	Bulldog - brindle	5	
1044	Bulldog - brindle	3	
1045	Bulldog - brindle white	6	1931
1046	Bulldog - brindle white	5	
1047	Bulldog - brindle white	3	
1072	Bulldog - white	6	1931
1073	Bulldog - white	5	
1074	Bulldog - white	3	
1176	Spotted Bulldog	6	
K 1	Seated Bulldog	2	
K 2	Seated Bulldog pup	2	
(168)	Robert Porter	6	1915
(210)	Robert Porter	6	1915
(180)	Louis Wearden & Guylee	3	1919
(288)	Girolamo Luxaroo	11	1932
	Ervan Lucas Bols	6	1940
6406	Bulldog with Union Jack L	6	1941-61
4607	Bulldog with Union Jack M	4	1941-61
	Bulldog with Union Jack S	2.5	1941
	Bulldog with sailor hat & cigar L	7	1941
	Bulldog with sailor hat & cigar M	5	1941
	Bulldog with sailor hat & cigar S	3	1941
	Bulldog with derby & cigar L	7.5	1941
	Bulldog with derby & cigar M	5	1941
	Bulldog with derby & cigar S	3	1941
	Bulldog with sailor suit & hat L	6	1941
	Bulldog with sailor suit & hat M	5	1941
	Khaki Bulldog & Union Jack L	6	1914
	Bulldog wall pocket	6.5	
	Bulldog matchstriker	3	
	Bulldog double matchstriker	3.5	

Matchstriker 3"

Wallpocket 6"

The seated Bulldog in the tin hat khaki glaze has sometimes been named for 'Old Bill', a character who was the embodiment of servicemen in the WWI trenches which appeared in cartoons by Bruce Bairnsfather (1888-1959)

HN 881
Bulldog, yachting hat and cigar 2.5"
A Bulldog Collection
Bulldog with Union Jack and eye patch
Bulldog with Union Jack, small size,

Cocker Spaniel HN 1021, Bulldog HN 129, K6, Peke HN 1040, Bulldog HN 881. Courtesy Phillips

THE DACHSHUND, originally from Germany, did not as the German Shepherd suffer the ignominity of a name change. In fact in the second world war 'Fritz' helped his glamourous mistress Jane to outwit and catch many German spies, in the pages of the popular 'Daily Mirror'. The Dachshund is renowned for his courage and scenting powers in the field but he has become a popular house pet. He is represented in the Championship range by *CH Shrewd Saint* occuring in six models. Three black and three red. The Poodle was another hunting dog which has become a favorite pet both in Britain and the United States. In 1954 there were more poodles registered at 'The Kennel Club' than any other breed and it stayed at the top of the popularity tree for several years. In 1955 a Poodle won Crufts 'Best in Show' but the Doulton Poodle was not given a championship name. The three Poodle models HN 2625-7 and the three Chow models HN 2628-30 although listed don't seem to have been issued.

The Doberman and the Boxer were two of the last breeds to be modelled and were both American dogs. Like the Labrador only the medium size of each were produced. The Doberman was modeled after *CH Rancho Dobe's Storm* but because the first model was not approved, Peggy Davies was asked to submit her version. She worked from photographs in this instance and her version was approved and issued in 1955.

The Labrador retriever was issued in a medium size only in 1967 but prototypes have been seen in three sizes. It was modelled by John Bromley from a black Labrador bitch, but does not in my opinion qualify as a female without her 'buttons'. *Bumblikite of Mansergh* was owned by Mrs M. Roslin-Williams whose Mansergh Kennels were famous for both fieldwork and show. Bumblikite was a champion in both spheres. She had had five litters of puppies when modelled, her puppies going all over the world. An excellent family dog, the Labrador is a keen worker too being one of the major breeds used as guide dogs for the blind and as 'sniffer dogs' in drug detection. The Labrador model has the distinction of being the last Champion produced and is I think the least successful representation of its breed. The series which was instituted by Charles Noke with Frederick Dawes in 1931 was finished by Jo Ledger and his team in 1967. All models were withdrawn by 1986. In the following table I have attempted to fill in some other issue and withdrawal dates. Some of these refer to withdrawal in the U.S.A.

The list is not confined to Championship dogs but it is very difficult to know where to draw the line. If you include the non-show stances such as the seated Cocker and pheasant why not mention the seated Scottie, Sealyham and Alsatian, all finely modeled dogs. Although the *Championship* list is complete we have mentioned only a few of the 'strays' if you look in the early HN numbers and amongst the character dogs you will find many Sealyhams and Fox Terriers amongst the mongrels. Happy hunting!

Dachsund HN 1127 HN 1139
Doberman HN 2645
Boxer HN 2643
Poodle HN 2631
Labrador HN 2667

The following table lists what is considered by most to be the Championship Series, the fifteen breeds first issued in 1931 and fifteen more added between 1938 and 1967.

		HN	ISSUED	DISCONTINUED		
				L	M	S
Cocker Spaniel	*'Lucky Star of Ware'*	1000	1931	60	85	69
Rough Haired Terrier	*Crackley Startler*	1007	1931	55	60	85
Scottish Terrier	*Albourne Arthur*	1008	1931	55	60	85
Pekinese	*Biddee of Ifield*	1010	1931 EXL	55	60	85
Airdale	*Cotsford Topsail*	1022	1931	60	85	69
English Foxhound	*Tring Rattler*	1025	1931	55	60	56
Sealyham	*Scotia Stylist*	1030	1931	55	55	60
Cairn	*Charming Eyes*	1033	1931	55	60	85
Bulldog		1042	1931	60	60	85
West Highland Terrier		1041	1931	60	-	-
English Setter	*Maesydd Mustard*	1049	1931	60	85	69
Irish Setter	*Pat o' Moy*	1054	1931	60	85	69
Collie	*Ashstead Applause*	1057	1931	60	85	69
Greyhound		1065	1931	55	55	60
Smooth Haired Terrier	*Chosen Don of Notts*	1068	1931	52	60	52
Gordon Setter		1079	1938	55	55	60
Dalmatian	*Goworth Victor*	1111	1938	55	85	69
Alsatian	*Benign of Picardy*	1115	1938	60	85	69
Dachshund	*Shrewd Saint*	1127	1938	55	69	69
Bull Terrier	*Bokus Brock*	1131	1938	52	60	52
Springer Spaniel	*Dry Toast*	2515	1938	55	67	85
American Foxhound		2524	1938	55	60	52
Welsh Corgi	*Spring Robin*	2557	1940	55	69	85
Great Dane	*Rebeller of Ouborough*	2560	1941	55	60	52
American Great Dane		2601	1941	55	60	52
Pointer		2624	1952	85	-	-
French Poodle		2631	1952	-	85	-
Boxer	*Warlord of Mazelaine*	2643	1952	-	85	-
Doberman Pinscher	*Rancho Dobe's Storm*	2645	1955	-	85	-
Labrador	*Bumblikite of Mansergh*	2667	1967	-	85	-
Cocker and pheasant		1001	1931	69	85	69
English Setter and pheasant		2529	1952	-	-	85

All designed by Frederick Daws except Pointer and Doberman Pinscher by Peggy Davies and the Labrador by John Bromley.

MINIATURE ANIMALS AND CHARACTER SERIES

There are quite a few groups of character animals which are great fun to collect. The set of six piglets and six kittens which were modelled by Peggy Davies for instance. Three face to the right and three to the left carefully planned so that they display well. The kittens also have two colourways. Three are ginger and three brown. The pigs are pale pink on a grassy mound.

CHARACTER KITTENS - Modelled by Peggy Davies

HN		HT	Dates	HN		HT	Dates
2579	Lying on back	1.5"	1941-1985	2582	On hind legs	3	1941-1985
2580	Licking back paw	2"	1941-1985	2583	Licking front paw	2	1941-1986
2581	Sleeping	1.5"	1941-1985	2584	Looking up	2	1941-1985

PIGLETS - Modelled by Peggy Davies

2648	Squatting	2	1959-1967	2651	Sleeping	1	1959-1967
2649	Standing	1.5	1959-1967	2652	Sitting	2	1959-1967
2650	Lying	1	1959-1967	2653	Rooting	1.5	1959-1967

In an interview with Louise Irvine in 1982 (R.D.I.C.C. Mag. Vol 2. No 4. Page 8) Peggy Davies told her that when she became an assistant to Cecil Noke in 1939:-

'I was first engaged in modelling a series of birds for him and then some tiny animal like *nesuke*. My place of work was next to his studio and part of it was a store for a collection of *flambé*. One day I borrowed a kitten to study whilst on my next project, the cat series which is still in production. Imagine my horror when it decided to climb in and out of the precious vases and up the staging containing them. Fortunately Mr Noke was a cat lover so all was well. As I recall in the brief period before I became a nurse for the war effort, I also modelled penguins, pigs and several other animals...'

So we know Peggy was responsible for the kittens, piglets and K penguins. But unfortunately we are not quite certain about the other K animals, the dogs, the hares and the birds. The larger sized *Dogs of Character* set is also unattributable at the moment. Peggy Davies although a cat person would have been very capable of producing models like the puppy at play with slipper, ball and bone. They are very much in the tradition of Cecil Aldin's dog illustrations and owe their inspiration to him. There are thirteen character dogs in the series including two sealyhams and two bull terriers. The first six were issued in 1934 and six more in 1937 and 1938. Obviously the pups at play were the best sellers and consequently in 1959 a further puppy playing with a slipper was added. At the same time seven others including the bull terriers and the sealyhams were withdrawn leaving six terrier pups which were in production until 1985 and are quite readily found. Those withdrawn in 1959 are of course the rarities. Between 1987-9 the playful pups were re-issued under the *Beswick* lable by the *Royal Doulton* group but the lack of detail makes them easily distinguishable from the originals.

These had two backstamps in the Royal Doulton range, the earlier one incorporating a printed HN number and a simpler roundel on the later ones as used on many other animal models.

46 HN2585 - HN2590

DOGS OF CHARACTER

HN		HT	
1097	Running with ball	2	1934-1985
1098	Lying on back	2	1934-1959
1099	Yawning	4	1934-1985
1100	Bull Terrier walking	4	1934-1959
1101	Lying yawning	2	1934-1959
1103	With ball	3	1934-1985
1158	With plate	3	1937-1985
1159	With bone	3.5	1937-1985
2508	Sealyham looking back	3	1938-1959
2509	Sealyham	2.5	1938-1959
2510	Running	3	1938-1959
2511	Bull Terrier	4	1938-1959
2654	With Slipper	3	1959-1985

A further six character studies of dogs are featured HN 2585- 2590. Four are terrier and cocker pups in two types of basket with a begging cairn and two sleeping cockers to complete the set, again nicely balanced subjects for display.

2585	Cocker in basket liver & white	2	1941-1985	2588	3 Terriers in basket	3	1941-1985
2586	Cocker in basket black & white	3	1941-1985	2589	Cairn begging	4	1941-1985
2587	Terrier in basket	3	1941-1985	2590	2 Cockers sleeping	2	1941-1985

These were issued for a long while and are available for collectors. However soon after were issued four *Lambs* HN 2595-2598 and six *Butterflies* HN 2604-2609 which are very rare indeed no doubt due to them being issued in 1941 at the outbreak of the second world war and the series not being revived after. There would have been very few made at this time.

There are various other sets made in the 20's and 30's which can only be collected with great difficulty such as:-

the *Character Penguins and Puffins* HN 256-266, 283-293. 22 pieces.

the *'Bonzo'* dog HN 808-813. 6 pieces.

Character Ducks HN 840-845. 6 pieces.

Miniature Birds HN 867-874. 8 pieces.

Character *Pigs in clown costume* HN 892-897. 6 pieces.

Young Elephants HN 949-952. 4 pieces.

Some of the miniature birds and ducks reappeared in the K series later.

Character Dog HN 2508
Character Dog HN 2510
HN 2606 from the Design book
Character Dog HN 1101

Mother and Child. Tusks wooden
and sold on a wooden plinth.
Flambe version lying down
Character dog HN 1097 with striped
or plain ball

Back row; K13, 3, 39, 12, 1, 11. Front Row; K 37, 22, 819.

THE K SERIES

There are 39 pieces in this series but collectors may wish to take only the section which reflects their main interest. There are 18 dogs all distinct breeds. 'Lucky' the cat K 12 comes in the middle of these. K 20 - K 25 is a series of six miniature penguins which are very popular with collectors. There are 11 rare birds and the list concludes with 3 hares. All are under 3" in height, the true miniature standard.

K. Penguins 22, 23, 25, 20, 24, 21.

K. Hares 37, 39, 38.

THE K SERIES

K		HT	DATES
1	Bulldog	2.5	1931-1977
2	Bulldog pup	2	1931-1977
3	Sealyham begging (760)	2.5	1931-1977
4	Sealyham lying	1	1931-1977
5	Airdale lying	1.5	1931-1977
6	Pekinese seated	2	1931-1977
7	Foxhound seated	2.5	1931-1977
8	Fox terrier seated	2.5	1931-1977
9	Cocker spaniel with bandage	2.5	1931-1977
10	Scottish Terrier begging	3	1931-1977
11	Cairn seated	2.5	1931-1977
12	'Lucky' black cat	2.5	1931-1976
13	Alsatian seated	3	1931-1977
14	Bull terrier lying	1.5	1940-1959
15	Chow	2	1940-1977
16	Welsh Corgi	2	1940-1977
17	Dachshund seated	2	1940-1977
18	Scottish terrier seated	2	1940-1977
19	St. Bernard lying	1.5	1940-1977
20	Penguin and chick	2	1940-1969
21	Penguin wings folded	2	1940-1969
22	Penguin head under wing	2	1940-1969
23	Penguin head down	1.5	1940-1969
24	Penguin wing out	2	1940-1969
25	Penguin standing	2	1940-1969
26	Mallard	1.5	1940-1946
27	Yellow Throated Warbler		1940-1946
28	Cardinal		1940-1946
29	Baltimore Oriole	3	1940-1946
30	Bluebird and lupins	2.5	1940-1946
31	Bullfinch		1940-1946
32	Budgerigar		1940-1946
33	Golden Crested Wren		1940-1946
34	Magpie		1940-1946
35	Jay	2	1940-1946
36	Goldfinch		1940-1946
37	Hare - on haunches	1.5	1940-1977
38	Hare - begging	2	1940-1977
39	Hare - on hind legs	1.5	1940-1977

'To Heel' leaflet 1933

DERIVATIVES - Bookends and Brooches, Plaques and Calenders, etc. etc.

Character Fox HN 963 2"

When your cabinets have rows of animals still more can be displayed on useful objects around the house. On my desk is a CALENDAR with a small character Fox. It is marked simply DOULTON. If you study Doulton catalogue pages from the 1930's you will find lots of novelties which include animals. The small size *Championship* dogs were mounted on alabaster BOOKENDS at 32/6 a pair. The Cocker and pheasant, in two colourways, were mounted on mahogany bookends at 36/- a pair. K dogs mounted on alabaster ashtrays were 10/- each but the best buy of all would have been the four DOG HEADS MOUNTED ON WOOD PANELS at 10/6 each. These heads were taken from the large size championship dog models and are very collectable today. Other heads are found mounted on DESK SETS and ASHTRAYS. They were also taken from the large size championship series but are flat at the base of the neck not the back. They also have a hole at the mouth. The purpose of the hole is questionable, maybe a pen or pencil holder, on the other hand I feel they are not suitable parasol handles as it is sometimes suggested. There is also a Fox Head mounted on a wood panel.

Irish Setter heads as mahogany bookends

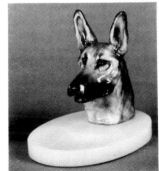

Alsatian head as pin tray

Fox
Pekinese
Cocker Spaniel
Irish Setter
Airdale
Sealyham

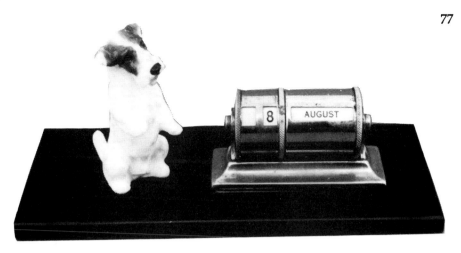

K3 as a calendar

K DOGS are found mounted as calendars, ashtrays and pen trays. They were also sold in combination with Doulton figurines. The *Old Balloon Seller and Bulldog* HN 1791 is familiar from its mention in *Royal Doulton Figures* (2nd edit. page 308) but here is a rarer duo *Paisley Shawl* HN 1460 with K 3 and there could be others.

An illustration here shows K 7 attached to a pottery ashtray, a more unusual combination. The K dogs are found as finials on tobacco jars but so are early character dogs like the hound and comic terrier here which are moulded in one with the lid. *Kingsware* tobacco jars are found with a Foxhound, a single Fox and another oval jar has the two curled Foxes.

Paisley Shawl HN 1460 and K3 1930s

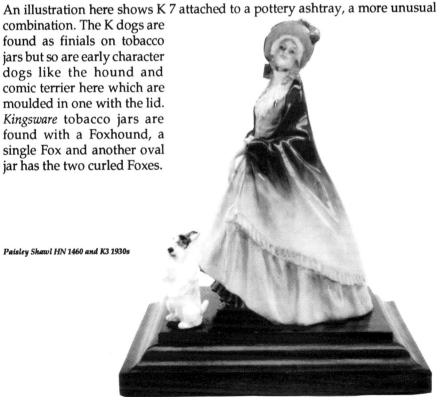

K7 as a pottery ashtray
Kingsware tobacco jar
Seated hound and comic terrier on tobacco jars

Mouse, Squirrel and Wren ashtrays and Robin HN 144

ASHTRAYS There are a series of these HN 1087-1095 with various small animals and birds cast in one with a china ashtray. There seem to be two shapes 154 and 155 and various colours for the tray ivory, orange and titanian. They are dated 1933/4. Unfortunately the china ashtrays didn't take the heat of a neglected cigarette very well and many are stained and cracked.

Pekinese HN 826 1923
Robin ashtray
Squirrel ashtray.
Courtesy Phillips

POTTERY COSTUME JEWELRY was popular in the 1930's and Royal Doulton made a range as did other factories like *Worcester* who stated that the brooches were intended for mounting on hats. A fashion which probably applied to the Doulton pieces too. 'Royal Doulton' is impressed on the brass pins only. There must be new discoveries to be made here. There are dogs, a persian cat, a kingfisher but in the Doulton design book foxes are mentioned but I have never found one. Desmond Eyles speaks of six Butterfly 'brooches' in *Doulton Burslem Wares* but again I have never seen one. However I may be speaking to a collector who has them all.

Brooches
Airdale

Persian Cat
Kingfisher
Courtesy Doulton

*Penguin flower holder in floating
bowl with clip-on butterfly*

Kingfisher flower holder HN 858

THE CLIP-ON BUTTERFLIES used in conjunction with 'floating' bowls are
quite easily found and come in yellow, blue and green. They are not always
marked and other firms did make them as they seem to have been a fashion
peculiar to the times.

FLOWER HOLDER animal
combinations are listed as
being made around 1923.
The subjects are mainly birds, a
duck, a heron, HN250 a Kingfisher, and a large Penguin
seen here in a lustre glaze. Mal-
lard HN 2544 has a vase
attached. There is an example
in the Sir Henry Doulton Museum.

Miniature birds mounted on onyx

TRINKET POTS were given animal finials, kingfishers again, monkeys, and a very desirable *Bulldog* HN 9987. The comic stylised puffins, penguins and other birds are found on bowls as well as being mounted independantly on ashtrays. The little curled Pekinese HN 826 seems to have been made specifically to be mounted in the centre of a rather classy circular onyx ashtray with a silver rim dated 1923. It was made for George Betjemen and Sons, London who commissioned quite a lot of quality things from Royal Doulton through the years. A small curled Cat was probably used in the same way. The two small Pekes HN 832 and 833 are often found mounted as are 'Bonzo' and 'Ooloo' and many others. The finds in this area must be endless and I have illustrated only a few here but I'm sure you will find others.

Miniature birds as finials

MOUNTED HEADS Wooden Plaques 4" high

		HT	1933
*	Airdale	3.5	
	Alsatian 898		
	Cairn		
*	Cocker Spaniel liver & white	3.5	
*	Cocker Spaniel blue roan	3.5	
	English Setter		
*	Foxhound		
*K22	Irish Setter	3.5	
*	Pekinese		
	Scottish Terrier		
*K27	Sealyham		
	Short Haired Terrier		
K34	Fox 804	3	

MOUNTED HEADS For Ashtrays And Penstands c1933

*898	Alsatian	3.5
*908	Cocker Spaniel liver & white	3
908	Cocker Spaniel blue roan	3
962	Fox Terrier	

BROOCHES 1"-2" High. c1933

Airdale		1	
Cairn		1.5	
Cocker Spaniel liver & white	LMS	2"1.5" 1"	
Cocker Spaniel black & white		LMS	
Foxhound		1	
Fox Terrier			
Greyhound two colours			
Pomeranian		1	
Sealyham		1.5	
Persian cat		1.5	
Kingfisher			
Fox			
Butterfly			

ASHTRAYS

		HT	1933-1934
*	Mouse 155	2.5	
*	Squirrel 155	3	
*1089	Wren 154	3	
	Robin 155	3	
	Rabbit	3	

Some heads were unmounted and have holes on the reverse for hanging

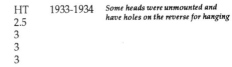

Spaniel brooch
Irish Setter head
Butterfly paperweight

HORSES

Royal Doulton were extremely fortunate in commissioning the services of William Chance to launch a series of horses in their range. A leader in his field and in great demand by owners of both sides of the Atlantic, he perfectly captured in clay some of the fastest and most valuable horses in the world. He exhibited his models at the Royal Acadamy and elsewhere. He created for Royal Doulton in the 1940's *Pride of the Shires, The Gude Grey Mare, The Chestnut Mare* and *Merely a Minor.* William Chance always modelled from life. The originals were taken from the best of their breeds in full consultation with their owners. The range remained until the 1960's and during that time the models sometimes

The Gude Grey Mare and Foal. Courtesy Louis Taylor

appeared in three sizes, different colourways and with or without a foal.

The Farmers Boy HN 2520 and *Dapple Grey* HN 2521 first issued in 1938 were again issued in 1942 and 1950 without their riders as HN 2578 and HN 2623. The modeller of *The Winner* HN 1407 is not yet recorded but he was very talented for it as a fine study of a race horse in full gallop straining every muscle. It is said to have been inspired by a swift bay mare named *Royal Doulton* by her owners the Rouston Brothers of Auckland, New Zealand. The horse won two gold cups and 4,325 sovereigns prize money. *The Winner* is portrayed as a grey in the figurine so their is some artistic licence. There is even more with the figure named *John Peel* HN 1408 also issued in 1930. John Peel who hunted with his hounds on foot in the steep fells of Cumbria in the late 18th century and early 19th century used a horse only as transport to and from the hunt site and never wore the 'pink' hunting dress but a coat of local grey cloth. The title of the figure was soon changed to that of *The Huntsman.* The horse ridden by *The Huntsman* HN 1815 and *Hunting Squire* HN 1409 is a very wooden animal. The artist is

not known but could hardly be by the same hand as that of *The Winner* which is worthy of William Chance.

In 1949 H.R.H. Princess Elizabeth, the present Queen, visited the Royal Doulton factory at Burslem and was presented with a model of *Monavene,* a steeple chaser owned jointly by the Princess and her mother the Queen, now the Queen Mother. Royalty must be the recipients of more unwanted gifts than most people but this must have been a delight to her. It was modelled by William Chance and painted on-glaze by Eric Webster who painted all the prototypes and was head painter of the Animal department. It was Eric Webster who painted the first Championship dog model in 1931. In the making of *Monavene* twenty six moulds were used with five firings for the colours. Apart from the presentation model there is one in *The Sir Henry Doulton Museum* at Burslem. If others were made they were for Royal Doulton's exhibition use only. *Monavene* is shown clearing a water jump. The following year William Chance modelled *Crinoline* but this was a prototype only and was bought with a photograph of Crinoline and its owner and a plaster cast from the original model by a lucky collector.

In 1966 the horse models were discontinued but in subsequent years the following entered the HN range. *Indian Brave* HN 2376 modelled by Peggy Davies was launched in a limited edition of 500 copies in 1967. The characteristically marked pony is ridden bare-back. *The Palio* HN 2428, Peggy Davies modelled for issue in 1971 was in contrast very elaborately caparisoned but the subject did not have the popular appeal of *Indian Brave* which had sold out and the full issue of 500 were never completed. A worthy addition to the range was the Horse Trooper and mount in *The Soldiers of the Revolution* series by Eric Griffiths. The model represents a sergeant in the Virginia 1st regiment Continental

Merely a Minor HN 2531 2537

Pride of the Shires HN 2563

Farmers Boy HN 2520

Punch Peon HN 2623

Refer to *Royal Doulton Figures* for models incorporating a figure

1407	*The Winner*	grey racehorse	L	7	1930-8
1408	*John Peel*	bay	L	8 3/4	1930-7
1409	*Hunting Squire*	grey	L	10	1930-7
1814	*The Squire*	grey	L	10	1937-c42
1815	*The Huntsman*	bay	L	8 3/4	1937-c42
William Chance Models					
2518	*Pride Of The Shires*	bay foal	L	9	1940-1960
2519	*The Gude Grey Mare*	bay foal	L	7	1940-1960
2520	*The Farmers Boy*	grey Shire	L	9	1938-60
2521	*The Dapple Grey*	grey Pony	L	7	1938-c42
2522	*The Chestnut Mare*	bay foal	L	6.5	1940-60
2523	*Pride Of The Shires*	grey foal	L	9	1940-60
2528	*Pride Of The Shires*	bay foal	L	9	1940-60
2530	*Merely A Minor*	bay racehorse	L	12	1940-c50
2531	*Merely A Minor*	grey	L	12	1940-c50
2532	*The Gude Grey Mare*	bay foal	M	5.5	1940-66
2533	*The Chestnut Mare*	bay foal	S	5	1940-60
2534	*Pride Of The Shires*	bay foal	M	6.5	1940-60
2536	*Pride Of The Shires*	grey foal	S		1940-60
2537	*Merely A Minor*	bay white socks	M	9.5	1940-60
2538	*Merely A Minor*	grey	M	9.5	1940-60
2563	*Pride Of The Shires*	bay	L	9	1940-60
2564	*Pride Of The Shires*	bay	M	6.5	1940-60
2565	*The Chestnut Mare*	bay	L	6.5	1940-60
2566	*The Chestnut Mare*	bay	M	5	1940-60
2567	*Merely A Minor*	grey	S	6	1940-66
2568	*The Gude Grey Mare*	grey hunter	L	7	1940-66
2569	*The Gude Grey Mare*	grey	M	5.5	1940-66
2570	*The Gude Grey Mare*	grey	S	4	1940-66
2571	*Merely A Minor*	bay	S	6	1940-66
2578	*Dapple Grey*	without rider grey	L	7	1942-60
2623	*Punch Peon*	without rider bay	L	7.5	1950-60
	Monaveen	bay steeple chaser	L	12	1949
	Crinoline	bay	L	?	1950 pilot
Peggy Davies Models					
2376	*Indian Brave*		Ltd edition 500	15.5	1967
2428	*The Palio*		Ltd edition 500	18	1971
Eric Griffiths Models					
2844	*Soldiers Of The Revolution*	bay	Ltd edition 350		14.5 1978

*The Chestnut Mare and Foal
HN 2533. Courtesy Louis Taylor*

*A pilot model of Crinoline with plaster cast of
original model and photograph of Crinoline.*

*Tankard 6" for Teofani Cigarettes
commemorating the 1937 Coronation Grand
National with the winner Royal Mail*

ART SCULPTURES

Raoh Schorr was a renowned sculptor of animals whom 'Jack' Noke commissioned to produce a range of Art Sculptures for Royal Doulton in 1936. In the main list I have found 22 different models by him, 8 of them so rare I have never seen a copy. That group was produced prior to the second world war which may account for their rarity. They do appear in a catalogue printed in the United States so perhaps at that time they were for export only.

The set of 13 animals by Schorr appear from time to time but even these are rare as they seem to have been an aquired taste. *The Sleeping Calf* is very reminiscent of this drawing by Schorr and is quite readily found probably because it has a more sentimental treatment. I don't think the set of 8 wild animals would have sold well even if there hadn't been a second world war. They were a bold experiment but did not mix happily with other Royal Doulton animal issues. None of the range was continued after the war.

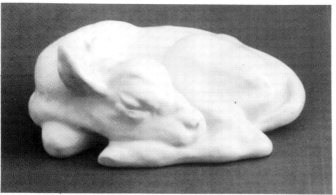

Sketch of sleeping calf.
Courtesy Phillips

Sleeping Calf
HN 1161

THE RAOH SCHORR RANGE

HN	HT		DATES
1130	Fox	11	1937-c1942
1145	Moufflon standing	6	1937-1942
1146	Calf sleeping	2	1937-1942
1147	Calf standing	6	1937-1942
1148	Buffalo	7	1937-1942
1149	Donkey - small	6	1937-1942
1150	Young Doe	4.5	1937-1942
1151	Swiss Goat	5	1937-1942
1152	Horse	6	1937-1942
1153	Moufflon lying	2	1937-1942
1154	Jumping Goat	7	1937-1942
1155	Donkey - large	6	1937-1942
1156	Suspicious Doe	6	1937-1942
1157	Antelope	6	1937-1942
2500	Cerval	8	1938
2501	Lynx	3.5	1938
2502	Deer - green	2	1938
2503	Deer - white	2	1938
2504	Lamb - green	2	1938
2505	Lamb - white	2	1938
2506	Asiatic Elephant	-	1938
2507	Wildebeest	-	1938

HN 1160 - HN 1172 same range in 'white matt'
HN 1173 - HN 1185 same range in natural colour
No HN numbers for 'black basalt' finish

I am the proud owner of the beautiful fox HN 1130 by Raoh Schorr, the first one in the series which has natural colouring in a semi-matt finish. In a Royal Doulton catalogue advertising the 13 semi domestic animals it mentions that they could be bought in a black basalt finish and I have seen copies but there are no HN numbers assigned to these. Desmond Eyles speaks of the range, "although highly regarded by the art critics they did not meet with much public response and had to be withdrawn during the war years."

Jumping Goat HN 1182

Fox HN 1130

Buffalo HN 1148

THE CHATCULL RANGE

Joseph Ledger A.R.C.A. who was Director of Design at Royal Doulton from 1955-1989 brought out a series of stylised animals in 1959. He named them *The Chatcull Range* for his home Chatcull Hall in Cheshire. The subjects were all quite gentle animals and were subtly painted in muted colours on bone china bodies. There were twelve in the set, nine of which were withdrawn in 1969. The three Siamese Cats continued in production until 1985. This set is collectable and has reasonable availability.

2655	Siamese Cat - seated	5.5	1960-1985
2656	Pine Marten	4	1960-1969
2657	Langur Monkey	4.5	1960-1969
2658	White Tailed Deer	5.5	1960-1969
2659	Brown Bear	4	1960-1969
2660	Siamese Cat - standing	5	1960-1985
2661	Mountain Sheep	5	1960-1969
2662	Siamese Cat - lying	4	1960-1985
2663	River Hog	3.5	1960-1969
2664	Nyala Antelope	5.5	1960-1969
2665	Llama	6	1960-1969
2666	Badger	4	1960-1969

Chatcull Range.
Not shown, White-tailed Deer, Mountain Sheep, and Siamese Cat seated and standing

Siamese Cat HN 2662

Robert Jefferson has been a naturalist all his life and his wildlife subjects are observed and sketched in the wild. Whereas Raoh Schorr and Jo Ledger used a simplistic stylised approach born in the studio, Robert Jefferson records and meticulously reproduces his subjects and their habitat in minute detail. The original models are sculpted in wax which gives finer detail than clay although it is more difficult to work. The *Snowshoe Hares* had more parts to the mould than any other piece Royal Doulton had made- with 119 castings.

ROBERT JEFFERSON ART SCULPTURES

HN		LTD	HT	DATE
2668	Puffins	250	11	1974
2669	Snowy Owl - male	150	16	1974
2670	Snowy Owl - female	150	9.5	1974
3500	Black-Throated Loon	150	11	1974
3501	White-Winged Cross Bills	250	7.75	1974
3502	King Eider	150	11	1974
3503	Roseate Terns	100	12.75	1974
3504*	Golden Crowned Kinglet	unltd	8	1974
3505	Winter Wren	unltd	5	1974
3506	Colorado Chipmunks	75	13.5	1974
3507	Harbour Seals	75	8.5	1975
3508	Snowshoe Hares	75	13	1975
3509*	Downy Woodpecker	unltd	7.5	1975
3510	Fledgling Bluebird	250	6	1976
3511	Chipping Sparrow	200	7.5	1976

Golden Crowned Kinglet HN 3504
Downy Woodpecker HN 3509

The Robert Jefferson art sculptures consist of 12 bird and 3 animal groups from North America. They were produced only for this market between 1974-6. 12 as limited editions of 75-250 in number with 3 models stated as being unlimited. With such intricacy they could never be produced in very large editions.

A WILDFOWL COUNTERFEIT
by
Lem Ward
GREATER SCAUP
MALE

HN 3514
ROYAL DOULTON

Greater Scaups HN 3514 HN 3517

Wooden decoy ducks have been employed for centuries in duck shooting and trapping. A model of the correct species is floated in sight of the guns hoping to entice that type of wild duck to the pond.

These eight models were based on the work of Lem Ward a famous American wood carver and are replicas of his own counterfeit carvings which are keenly sought by collectors and are extremely desirable and expensive in the U.S.A. However the replicas did not prove as popular and had a short run. They were gift boxed in the USA.

LEM WARD - A WILDFOWL COUNTERFEIT   HT 3-4"

HN		DATES
3512	Mallard - male	1979-1985
3513	Pintail - male	1979-1985
3514	Gtr. Scaup - male	1979-1985
3515	Mallard - female	1979-1985
3516	Pintail - female	1979-1985
3517	Gtr. Scaup - female	1979-1985
3518	Mercanser - male	1980-1985
3519	Mercanser - female	1980-1985
3520	Green Wing Tail - male	1981-1985
3521	Green Wing Tail - female	1981-1985

IMAGES OF NATURE

A series of animal studies in a 'modernist' style first issued in a white bone china body in 1982. In the *Royal Doulton Flambé* exhibition at the R.D.I.C.C. gallery, London, in 1983 a range of flambé prototypes of the above were shown. They were presented to exhibitors at the end of the show and since then some have been introduced into the range.

HN		HT	ARTIST	DATES
3522	*The Leap* - Dolphin	9	Adrian Hughes	1982-
3523	*Capricorn* - Mountain Goat	10	Adrian Hughes	1982-
3524	*The Gift Of Life* - Mare & Foal	9	Russell Willis	1982-
3525	*Courtship* - Terns	15	Russell Willis	1982-
3526	*Shadow Play* - Cat	10	Russell Willis	1982-

IMAGES OF NATURE

3527	*Going Home* - two Geese	6	Adrian Hughes	1982-
3528	*Freedom* - Otter	8.5	Robert Jefferson	1983-6
3529	*Bright Water* - two Otters	8.5	Robert Jefferson	1983-6
3530	*Clear Water* - Otter	8.5	Robert Jefferson	1983-6
3531	*Nestling Down* - Swans	13	Adrian Hughes	1986-
3532	*The Homecoming* - Doves	15	Russell Willis	1987-
3533	*Patience* - Heron	12	Peter Gee	1987-
3534	*Playful* - Lion Cubs	7.5	Adrian Hughes	1987-
3535	*Courtship* - Flambé	15	Russell Willis	1987-
3536	*The Gift of Life* - flambé	9	Russell Willis	1987-
3538	*Nestling Down* - flambé	13	Adrian Hughes	1988-
3539	*The Homecoming* - flambé	15	Russell Willis	1990-
3540	*Graceful* - two Panthers	111	John Ablitt	1989-
3542	*Serenity* - shoal of fish	11	John Ablitt	1990-
3543	*Friendship* - Borzoi & Cat	8	John Ablitt	1990-
3547	*Pegasus* Lawley's By Post Ltd. Edit.	11	Alan Malankowski	1990

Measurements include wooden plinth.

Hind and Calf 6" Model 2419

Badger HN 2666

ANIMALS IN ADVERTISING

Advertisers are always fond of using animals to present their message. The appealing puppy and kitten must have swelled the collecting boxes made at Lambeth for *The Royal Society for the Protection of Cruelty to Animals,* R.S.P.C.A. Doulton themselves used a rather bad tempered kitten to advertise their architectural *Carrara* finishes, which clad so many buildings from *the Savoy Hotel* to the local *Odeon* in the years 1885-1939.

RSPCA collecting boxes

Doulton Carrara paperweights

McMullens "Silver Seal" Port ashtray
Old Crow Whisky decanter
Doulton design book
Robert Porter display
Bulldog

Many other firms used dogs, cats, birds and bears quite indiscriminately to promote their goods. Some like *Old Crow* bourbon; *Grouse* whisky; *Silver Seal* port, and *Bulldog* guiness used representations of their trade marks to sell their liquor.

*Giralamo Luxardo
decanters*

Grouse Whisky decanter
Evan Lucas Bols decanter
Louis Wearden and Guylee
display model

The bulldog, salmon and pekinese figural bottles made at Burslem for the Dutch firm of *Ervan Lucas Bols* and the bulldog and polar bear flasks for *Girolama Luxardo* distillers of Zara, Yugoslavia are very attractive. The manufacturers must have realised their appeal as ornaments once the contents were drunk. These five flasks are extremely rare today. The Bulldog flask for *Girolama Luxardo* was an adaptation of the usual seated model which appears so often and in various guises throughout the animal lists. It was adorned with the Union Jack which is not shown in the design book drawing. Rather a strange choice for a foreign firm. The same seated Bulldog with Union Jack was a very suitable choice for the Bradford firm of 'Louis Wearden and Guylee Ltd', to advertise their drill chucks.

The last bulldog was a paperweight or a shop display model as were the *Robert Porter* Bulldog and the *Stauffer* terrier. The begging dog with a sugar cube on his nose was adapted from a model in the HN series. All these models would have been presented to customers as were the *Carrara* models given away by Doulton. No doubt *McMullen's* gave their *Silver Seal* ashtrays to lucky victuallers. The body of the seal has a lustrous glaze in keeping with the name.

Penguin books
A Partridge in an
F.T. 'Financial Times'
Stauffer Watch Dog

The 1930's were competitive times and free gifts were often offered as buying incentives. Sixty soap wrappers in exchange for a *Wrights Coal Tar* dragon fly soap dish does seem a lot but they must have given good service as there are so many around today.

A paper lable on the wooden base of the *R.S.P.C.A.* collecting boxes say they were 'the property of the society'. I often dream of finding that there is still a dusty storeroom somewhere full of the returned boxes.

Two recent Doulton productions are worthy successors to the earlier pieces. Made for *Penguin* books and *The Financial Times* who are both associate companies of *Royal Doulton Ltd* as all three are part of the larger *Pearson* group of companies.

LAMBETH MODELS

ADVERTISER	ANIMAL	HT	ITEM	DATE
Doulton Carrara	Polar Bear	6.5	paper weight	c1890
	Kitten	6	paper weight	
	Horse	6	paper weight	
R.S.P.C.A.	Persian Kitten	8.5	collecting box	c1900
	Labrador Pup	**7.5**	collecting box	
Mcmullens 'Silver Seal' Port	Seal Lion	3	ashtray	c1910
Wrights Coal Tar Soap	Dragon Fly	4"w	soap dish	c1920
Samual Jones & Co. Ltd.				
Camberwell Beauty		(20'x14')	tile mural	1948

BURSLEM MODELS

Robert Porter & Co. Ltd. 1915	Bulldog (168)	6	blue or brown print	1915
	(210)	6		
Louis Wearden & Guylee Ltd.	Bulldog (180)	3	display model	1919
Stauffer & Son & Co. Watchmakers	Begging Dog	8	display model	1929
Daily Mirror Children's Page	Wilfred (922)	4	display model	1928
Daily Mirror Pip, Squeak &	Wilfred (935)	4	display model	1930
Artandia Ltd. Spain	Cockatoo	15	loudspeaker cover	c1930
Girolama Luxardo Distillers	Polar Bear	10.5	liquor flask	1932
Girolama Luxardo Distillers	Bulldog (288)	11	liquor flask	1932
Ervan Lucas Bols Distillers	Bulldog (37)	6	liquor flask	1940
Ervan Lucas Bols Distillers	Leaping Salmon	9.5	liquor flask	1940
Ervan Lucas Bols Distillers	Pekinese	6	liquor flask	1940
National Distillers Corp Usa	*Old Crow*	14	liquor flask	1954
Mathew Gloag & Son. Ltd. Distillers	Grouse	9.5	liquor flask	1983
Whyte & Mackay Distillers	Peregrine Falcon	6.5	liquor flask	1979
Whyte & Mackay Distillers	Short Eared Owl	6.5	liquor flask	1984
Penguin Books	Penguin	4.5	bookend	
The Financial Times A Partridge in an F.T.		2.5	paperweight	1988
			ltd edit. 1,200 box cert.	
Carrara	Horse		modelled by Mark Marshall.	
Carrara	Bear		probably by Leslie Harradine.	

Last four Burslem items modelled by Graham Tongue.
Lambeth tile panel designed by Edward Eggleton.
For further details see *Doulton Burslem Advertising Wares* by Jocelyn Lukins 1985

Wrights Coal Tar Soap dish

The Royal Doulton Advertising Lion
21" Burslem c.1952

Do visit *The Camberwell Beauty* tile panel in south London sometime. It is now attractively re-sited after the demolition of the former Samuel Jones factory which made Butterfly Brand tapes nearby in Camberwell.

The Camberwell Beauty tile pannel 1948

ANIMALS IN SERIESWARE

There are over fifty seriesware designs which feature animals and multiplying that by the number of scenes in each series and the number of different shapes found you find the pieces to collect are endless.

If you choose Dogs you have a few series which show definite breeds such as *Scottish Terrier* D 5386 one of a set of six issued in 1936 which is quite readily found. Unfortunately a set of six dogs heads D 5259 issued the same year seem to be elusive. Dogs forming part of the design are more readily found like the *Cotswold Shepherd's* faithful Collie D 5561 1933 and the sportsman's retrievers in *Scottish Hunting Scenes* D 3692 1913.

Plough Horses D2877 1906
Setter heads
Scottish Terrier D53861933
Dogs and Game, Pheasants D3544 1900

Some horses form the whole design such as *Plough Horses* D 2877 1908. But many are found pulling farm carts and coaches or accompanied by packs of hounds in the many fox hunting series.

There are a few cats from Souter's smug character cats and the amusing stylised jug design D 2340 1906 by an unknown artist to the companionable moggy of *Open Door* D 3750 1914.

Most domestic animals appear on seriesware and wild animals are represented in the photographic views from the Kruger national park in an *African* series in production for many years between 1936 and 1975. Birds, fishes and butterflies abound in seriesware and you can choose your subject.

Finely hand painted game and fish plates were also produced at Burslem in the early part of this century.

Plates make a very good background for your animal collection and can set a scene and bring more interest.

Here are just a few suggestions.

Cotswold Shepherd D5561 1933
Elephant Box D 5526 5" 1935

Desert Scenes D3192 1909
Heraldic Cats jug D2340 1906

Hunting Man plate, embossed Fox-Hunting coffe pot 1912, Quorn Hunt teapot 1924, Huntsman Fox HN 6448 5" Withdrawn 1985

Coaching Days, 1905-1955
Cigarette-boxes. Old English Hunting Scenes 1953,
Charles Simpson's, Hunting D6184 1947.
Owl wall-pocket D5772 1937

Reynard the Fox 1935

American Birds H1422 1927

Cockerel teapot 6" 1938

Monarch of the Glen. Dewar's decanter c.1916
Swans D 5206 1932

Greyhound on Hare Coursing spirit barrel c.1914
Crow wall-pocket D5772 1937

Kookaburra and Kangeroo Paw dish D4206 1920

CARTOON STARS

In the main list are five figures which reproduce contempory cartoon characters. The earliest is *Kateroo* HN154, a large striking 13" figure of a very smart cat in all senses of the word. He has his own very definite black and white marking as he appeared in his cartoons but a green-bronze and a yellow version exists. Doulton always experimented in different effects and the animal models can be found as any other Doulton pieces in many surprise glazes.

Kateroo pintray
Kateroo HN 154

KATEROO was the invention of David Henry Souter, 1862-1935, British born he emigrated to Australia in his early twenties. He published his cartoons in the Sydney *Bulletin* for 40 years using his character cat, *Kateroo* as a comment on society. From 1906 until 1936 Doulton produced many designs with the adventures of this cantankerous cat including a pin tray collected by many dealers, and a set of six very appealing plates telling the story of *Kateroo's* courtship and marriage.

Kateroo sketch

The Wedding Tour

BONZO HN 808-812, 814 and 815, is a tiny 2"
figure which appears in many colourways, including ivory with red buttons
or black buttons, with black and brown patches and a deep blue glaze. The
figure is so small it only carries DOULTON and sometimes the model number
868 is decipherable but there is no room for an HN number. He is very often
mounted on trays. Doulton gave this model an experimental glaze *Chinese jade*
which of course makes him appear even more of a blob. He was created by
George Studdy, 1878-1925, who was a quiet modest man but his illustrative
work was adventurous and his most famous creation the mischievous dog
Bonzo became a star of the comic strip, magazines and post cards. In 1924 he
advertised lady's suspenders in *Good Housekeeping*. George Studdy was an early
animator (1914) and *Bonzo* appeared in 26 films.

OOLOO HN 818, 819 was another Studdy character issued about the same time
as *Bonzo* in only two colourways. He should have been in the black and white
markings as he appeared in his cartoons only. He always wore a big grin as did
Bonzo who appeared in flesh pink in his cartoons.

Ooloo appeared in *The Sketch* magazine in 1929 and became 'the Sketch cat'.
Doulton also reproduced 'Miss Sketch' a pedlar figure which always appeared
on the front cover, as a figurine, although
she has become familiarly known as *the
Sketch girl*.

These early examples like *Bonzo* are rare
today, as they were produced in the 1930's
and were not made after the outbreak of
the second world war and so had short
runs. However *Ooloo* was adapted as *Lucky
K 12* which remained in production until
1976.

Bonzo 2"
Courtesy Bonham's

Ooloo gives his blessing to a Fancy Dress Ball. The 'Sketch' and Studdy cat featured on the programme of the Stage Ball which takes place at Covent Garden on Thursday March 7th 1909 under distinguished patronage, for Ooloo is among the many people who are taking an active interest, as this programme shows. The festivity will, in a way, be a coming-out dance, for he recently made his debut in 'The Sketch', and has not as yet put in an appearance at any important public function

Bonzo advertising Sphere Suspenders in 1924. Bonzo in Chinese Jade

Pip, Squeak and Wilfred HN 935 mounted with a tray and *Wilfred* HN 922 standing on a basket of carrots, typically blowing his own trumpet, were probably commissioned items by *The Daily Mirror's* children's club. Doulton also produced a range of nursery ware for the Daily Mirror like the small plate shown here.

B.J. Lamb created one of the earliest and best-loved British newspaper strips *Pip, Squeak and Wilfred* and it was drawn by A.B. Payne and appeared in *The Sunday Pictorial* and *The Daily Mirror*, from 1919-1955 with a break during world war two when cartoons were not allowed as newsprint was in short supply. *Pip, Squeak and Wilfred*, a dog, a rabbit and a penguin, appeared on the children's page. B.J. Lamb was 'Uncle Dick' and wrote the page and instituted a children's club.

CECIL ALDIN 1870-1935

Anyone who knows London will be familiar with its typical town houses. White stucco on four to six floors with a few steps up to a pillared door. Kensington and it environs has many streets, squares and crescents with some of the best of these houses. Four hundred of them were built by Cecil Aldin's father and grandfather. He was brought up in some comfort in one of them and at the age of six looking out from an upstairs nursery he saw and sketched his first horses as they passed by in the street. Taken for walks in nearby Kensington Gardens he watched the elegant riders trotting by. Even in these very early days he had a humorous approach and loved to show riders falling off their mounts into the mud. His favorite books were always on horses and hunting and Randolf Caldecott's illustrations to *John Gilpin* were familiar to him. Hunting became a passion with him from the age of thirteen.

He was not a good scholar and not even very good at 'Art' and it was obvious he was not intended for a business career. His father, Charles Aldin who had had no choice but to enter the family business and yet was an enthusiastic amateur artist, decided to give his son art training. Nearby Melbury Road was the

home of many leading artists and Cecil became a pupil of Albert Moore. However drawing classical ladies was not his forte and at 16 he moved to the art school at South Kensington which is now *The Royal College of Art*. Whatever subject he was working at he usually surrounded it with a doodled frieze of action sketches of horses and dogs. Later he moved to the country to study with a specialist in animal art Frank Calderon. Here he was at last completely happy. He had a remarkable teacher and he could work at the subjects close to his heart. The studio was a large timbered barn at Midhurst in Sussex, a village with a wealth of old timbered buildings which he

Old English Scenes D 4507. Courtesy Phillips

loved to sketch. The local butcher had a motley collection of 'hounds' and he sometimes loaned Cecil a carthorse to follow the hunt for foxes, rabbits or whatever was about.

Whilst at Midhurst he developed rheumatic fever which left him with a weak heart and he returned to London where almost immediately he had his first drawing published in *The Building News* for Sept. 1890. It showed a cosy fireside in a Sussex pub with fireDOGS made by the local blacksmith, for which Aldin received his first fee of ten shillings. Soon he received three guineas from *The Graphic* for drawings of dogs at the *St. Bernard Club* show. Encouraged by this success and a small allowance from his family he rented a studio in Chelsea. Success came slowly but drawings of his in *The Illustrated London News* and *The Pall Mall Gazette* attracted the attention of Sir Douglas Straight who asked him to illustrate Kiplings *Jungle Stories* which he was publishing in his magazine *The Pall Mall Budget*. The first book he illustrated was *Spot, an autobiography* in 1894. He illustrated other Kipling stories and used as models the animals in Regents Park Zoo. He became a success. His drawings were well suited to magazine reproduction and work flowed in.

Cecil Aldin always gregarious gathered a circle of artist friends around him. With three of them Dudley Hardy, Phil May and Tom Browne and others he formed *The London Sketch Club*. Their evenings of sketching, smoking conversazione's, suppers and fancy dress balls were lively affairs. Aldin's close friend John Hassall soon joined them and on the previous page is a character sketch of one friend by another.

This was the great day of the illustrator and poster artist. Photography had not yet replaced the artist in these fields. Aldin and his colleagues were kept very busy and the work they produced is still familiar to us today. Hassall, Dudley Hardy, Studdy, Rowntree and Aldin all friends at the *London Sketch Club* sold designs to Royal Doulton. Aldin's posters for *Colman's* mustard and *Cadbury's* cocoa are classics today. His coaching and hunting prints and the most lucrative set of all *Old Inns* are familiar still and very collectable. When he has earning as much as £400 a year, he married and he and his wife Rita,

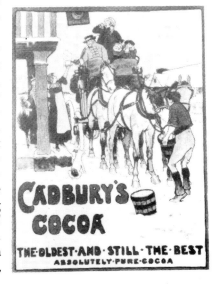

a bulldog, a borzoi and a terrier moved to Bedford Park in Chiswick, London. The area had a Bohemian reputation and the Aldin's fitted in well and made even more friends. He kept a horse in his back yard and set off from Bedford Park to hunt with the West Surrey Staghounds. The 'backyard' in an English house doesn't correspond to its namesake in Australia and the U.S.A., it was a small area with a lean-to bicycle shed but in it Aldin kept various horses, and a donkey. In due time he added a son and a daughter to the *menage* and they inspired him to produce designs for toy wooden horses and other animals. Having painted a freize of animals around his own children's nursery, he and Hassall produced a series of lithographed nursery freizes. The complete freize consisted of seven panels five feet long. Aldin did a hunting freize for libraries, smoking rooms and billard rooms. *Liberty's* exhibited model nurseries decorated with the freizes and the Queen of Spain decorated the royal nursery with an Aldin freize.

Cecil Aldin got into conversation with Walter Emmanuel quite by chance on the pavement outside a publishers office and they agreed to colaborate on a book Emmanuel had written about his dog, *A Dog Day*. It was the first of other collaborations between them and *A Dog Day* alone sold 100,000 copies before Emmanuel's death in 1915 and was continually reprinted. Emmanuel introduced Aldin to *Punch* and he illustrated Emmanuel's *Dogs of War* which first appeared in the magazine.

It is six of the illustrations done for *A Dog Day* which are reproduced in the Royal Doulton seriesware *Aldin's dogs* introduced in 1926. The same year Doulton introduced *Old English Scenes* and introduced it as 'specially drawn for Doulton & Co. Ltd. by Cecil Aldin'. Although these are the only designs commissioned by Doulton many other series are strongly influenced by him, such as Victor Venner's *Coaching Days* and William Grace's *Old English Coaching Scenes*. Then of course the playful pups character dog series owe a lot in inspiration to his dog illustration, and their title to a book he published in 1927 *Dogs of Character*. The books Aldin illustrated and the posters and etchings he produced are too numerous to mention here but are all listed in an excellent book *Cecil Aldin the story of a sporting artist* by Roy Heron 1981. He illustrated Charles Dickens *Pickwick Papers, Black Beauty* and his favorite book *Handly Cross* (or *Mr Jorrocks Hunt*). Most of his illustrations incorporated his favorite subjects, hunting and coaching scenes, and old timbered inns and houses. It was said of him, 'he usually manages to get a dog into the picture somewhere'.

A·DOG·DAY

BY
WALTER
EMANUEL
PICTURED BY
CECIL
ALDIN

London · William Heinemann Ltd. 1926

He produced more successful books with Emmanual including *A Gay Dog* 1905 and *Jack and Jill*, where Jack was a mongrel dog and Jill a tabby cat. His household always consisted of horses and dogs which were at hand to act as his models. He loved wolfhounds, bull terriers, bulldogs, dalmatians, sealyhams and rough and smooth haired terriers, and all. At one time in Bedford Park he had thirteen dogs, two monkeys and a fox cub. He exercised and played with them every day and they were trained to keep quiet when the master was at work. There are many photographs of Cecil Aldin and there is always a dog in the picture somewhere. It was his stable which forced him to move out of London in 1904 to Henley-on-Thames and later to Purley. He would have liked to have been born a country gentleman riding to Hounds. At last he had realised this life-style and could now indulge his passion for hunting to the full. He was well known and popular wherever he went. He became a master of foxhounds just before the first world war.

Aldin's Dogs. Celadon plate

When war broke out he was appointed purchasing officer in charge of a remount group providing horses for the army. Captain Aldin stabled up to 300 horses at a time. Against army scepticism he employed an all girl staff of stablehands including his wife and daughter. This practice was later taken up by other remount groups over the country.

A fellow student from Midhurst days came to join him, Alfred 'Bill' Munnings. He was unfit to become soldier as he had lost an eye but he was an expert horseman and a great asset.

Later Munnings went to France as an official war artist and of course was knighted, became President of *The Royal Acadamy* and more famous even than Aldin for his paintings of horses.

Dudley Aldin who had inherited his father's charm, artistic abilities and red hair was killed in action in France in 1916 aged 19. Cecil with difficulty worked on at a stage adaptation of his *Happy Family* books for children. He designed scenery and costumes and produced the musical play which was subtitled *Cecil Aldin's Animals at Play* (it gave Noel Coward one of his first roles). Nine years later he produced a play with more live animals on the stage, including horses and hounds and the set design by Aldin was an old coaching inn. In the 1920's he hunted in the summer on Exmoor in the West Country. At Porlock he started his own *Comic Mongrel*

Titanian vase. Courtesy Phillips

116

"The Cecil Aldin Series." D 4507.

Specially drawn for Doulton & Co., Ltd. by Cecil Aldin

OLDOLD ENGLISH SCENES PRODUCED BY THE INIMITABLE PENCIL OF CECIL ALDIN

No artist has a more perfect knowledge of the old half-timbered house and all it;'s associations than he. A hunting man himslef, he posesses an intimate aquaintance with the horse and the hound, and his wonderful pictures of Parson and Squire in panelled room or on horseback are like a breath of fresh invigorating country air.

Dotted along the main road these picturesque old houses lend a character and a dignity to the landscape and a pleasant background to huntsman and hound as well as the more homely rustic types.

These scenes have been drawn by Cecil Aldin himself specially for reproduction in this interesting series - every piece bearing his signature.

Royal Doulton Potteries, Burslem, Stoke on Trent
From a contemporary Doulton advertisement.

Doulton catalogue page
Courtesy Royal Doulton

Aldin's Dogs Pintray

Dog Show which had so many classes every dog could become a winner. He had classes for 'the longest tail' or 'the dog with most spots'. He was not fond of the champion show dog and its creators and this was his protest. His flow of books continued in the 1920's and '30's but because of ill health he moved to Majorca in 1930.

Aldin missed England, his hunters and countryside. Six of their dogs went with them and 'Susan', the sealyham was soon chasing little green lizards instead of rats and mice. The Aldin's designed and built a studio and Aldin continued to sketch his by now world famous models although handicapped by severe arthritis. He wrote his autobiography *Time I Was Dead* 1934 and when travelling to England late that year he had a heart attack. He continued to sketch from his hospital bed until he died in January 1935. 'Cracker', his bull terrier howled mournfully in Majorca before news of his master's death was received there. Rita Aldin stayed on in Majorca with 'Cracker' and the other dogs until 'Cracker' died 2.5 years later. He was reported in the press as being, 'the most famous animal model in the world' and his obituary appeared in *The Times*. At a memorial exhibition of his work, it was written of Aldin 'he loved painting dogs, and probably no painter of today, or yesterday ever caught the soul of dogdom as Cecil Aldin did'.

Dogs of Character HN 1158, 1159

Sketches from "A Dog Day"

ANIMALS AND FIGURES by Doug Pinchin

The British are a nation of animal lovers. One of the emblems of the nation is a Bulldog so that it should not come as too much of a surprise to see that the Royal Doulton collection of figurines reflects this national obsession. What is amazing is the sheer variety, not to mention quantity of figures which incorporate an animal in their design. The advent of animals is not confined to one style of figure or even one period of production. The most cursory examination of the range will reveal animals getting in on the act in most styles of figures from the art deco type like *Lido Lady* HN 1220 with her pekinese to street sellers such as the *Windmill Lady* HN 1400 with her affectionate bassett hound.

The use of the animals with figures dates from the earliest days of production. *Milking Time* HN 3 issued in 1913, depicts a country girl about to milk her goat. *Pussy* HN 18 touchingly portrays a young girls affection for her cat, the first of our feline friends to be featured. Coming more up to date *Andrea* HN 3058, plays with a fluffy white cat, while a ginger tom is *The Favorite* HN 2249 eagerly awaiting a saucer of milk from his elderly owner. Cats are again shown in their almost traditional role as companions to more mature ladies in the figures, *Twilight* HN 2256 where the grey cat is playfully destroying the old woman's ball of wool and *Forty Winks* HN 1974 where a black and white 'London cat' stands guard over his snoozing mistress the rarer companion fireside figure *Uncle Ned* HN 2094 has a spaniel-type figure for company. These homely 'moggies' are in something of a contrast to the sleek feline playing with some lace in the recent *Dorothy* HN 3098.

Lido Lady HN 1220

The choice of an animal added to a figure has not always been so cosy and domestic. Indeed some combinations are more than a little bizarre. In 1913 the figure known as *Child on Crab* HN 32 was introduced. To our eyes this curious combination may seem strange. It appears to have been based on *Baby* HN 12 this accounts for the human element. There was a children's book of the time with that title which would mean the concept was more familiar to collectors in 1913. It could hardly have been a runaway success as only three copies were made in 1916 compared with 148 of the popular *Darling* HN 1. It must have been considered a success in some way because in 1920 another similarly

strange pairing was introduced, *Boy on a Crocodile* HN 373, both of these groups were the work of Charles Noke as was *Boy on a Pig* HN 1369.

Leaving aside these rather esoteric combinations there are other less exotic but nevertheless effective teamings of humans and their pets. There are the very stylish art deco combinations. The ladies are very much of their time and the choice of accompanying dogs gives an insight into canine fashions of the period. *Scotties* HN 1281 depicts a chic young 'flapper' complete with bobbed hair, a modern frock and two up to the minute accessories, a pair of Scottish terriers. The alternative colourway HN 1349 is also named *Scotties* but as part of the colour variation affects the dogs which change from black to off-white, perhaps the figure should have been re-named 'Westies' to take into account that Scottish terriers are always black and West Highland Terriers white. Then such details are not always of great importance to the designers at Burslem.

Boy on a Crocodile HN 373

Boy on a Pig HN 1369

Scotties HN 1281 1928

The addition of a dog accounts for the re-numbering and re-naming of two figures. Take an *Irish colleen* HN 766 add a German shepherd dog, change the colour of the girls outfit and the group becomes *Moira* HN 1347. *Rosamund* HN 1320 underwent a similar metamorphosis to become *Iona* HN 1346. Again the choice of dog reflects contempory canine fashions.

The idea of dogs accompanying stylish figures has been revived in the *Reflections* series. The Greyhound in *Strolling* HN 3073, the Afghan Hound in *Promenade* HN 3072, *Park Parade* HN 3116 with her Borzoi and a suitably chunky Samoyed out for *A Winters Walk* HN3052 all add to the period feel of the figures.

Moira HN 1347 1929

Earlier periods of history have been evoked by *the Queens of the Realm* limited edition figures. Of the set of four queens, *Queen Victoria* HN 3125 has proved most popular because Pauline Parsons shows her as a young woman playing with King Charles Spaniels rather than the stern 'Widow of Windsor'. Victoria was very fond of King Charles Spaniels and the first one she had was called 'Dash'. He had been given to her mother, the Duchess of Kent, by Sir John Conroy in January 1833. Three months later Victoria had adopted 'dear sweet little Dash'. The poor dog must have been good natured as Victoria is reported to have dressed him up in a scarlet jacket and blue trousers!

Queen Victoria HN 3125 1987

Pauline Parsons has also modelled the 'Queen for a Thousand Days', *Anne Boleyn* HN 3232 second wife of Henry VIII. She is shown with the dogs a spaniel and her greyhound pet, 'Urian', whom Henry condemned for his satanic name, when he accused Anne of being in league with the devil amongst other trumped up charges which allowed him to have her executed. The Greyhound is appropriate to this Tudor figure as Edmond Tudor, grandfather of Henry VIII, the founder of the Tudor dynasty was created Earl of Richmond in 1453 and used a white greyhound as his badge. Consequently the white greyhound of Richmond held great heraldic significance for all the Tudor monarchs. It became one of *The Queens Beasts*. The set of these heraldic emblems made for the coronation of the present queen can be seen in Kew Gardens, near Richmond. The Spaniel was always popular at the French court where Anne Boleyn spent her girlhood.

The Welsh Corgi is known to be a favorite of the present royal family. The first of this particular royal line has been immortalised again by Pauline Parsons in a recent figure of *H.M. Queen Elizabeth the Queen Mother as the Duchess of York* HN 3230 as it includes a portrait of 'Dookie' the first royal corgi.

A far from regal dog but this time taken from life is seen at the vets in Bill Harper's *Thanks Dog* HN 2731. The Collie is the likeness of Bill's own pet 'Laddie'.

In complete contrast to the robust good nature of the Collie, a dog of miniature proportions, a Chihuahuas, is being petted by the stately *Charlotte* HN 2421.

Our canine friends also predominate in many child studies in the HN range. Young children often have a special affinity for animals, particularly household pets. A bond sometimes develops between child and pet as they grow up together, building a special trust between them. This unique relationship is graphically shown in the *Childhood Days* series. A young would-be nurse is bandaging her canine patient in *It Won't Hurt* HN 2963 and a young master valiantly attempts to bath his long suffering hound in *Please Keep Still* HN 2967. Earlier figures also show this special relationship between pet and young owner; *Golden Days* HN 2274 has her terrier, *My Pet* HN 2238 a dog of rather indeterminate breed and *Welcome Home* HN 2167 is receiving a warm welcome from her fluffy Samoyed. A dog of great scale is featured in *Buddies* HN 2546. The Great Dane dwarfs his young master in an attitude of benign protection.

The Queen Mother as Duchess of York HN 3230 Courtesy Lawleys by Post

Buddies HN 2543

Animals have been added to figures to help convey the subject of the piece. The nursery rhyme character *Old Mother Hubbard* HN 2314 is identified by her mongrel dog with its bone. Bo-peep is associated with sheep and the first Doulton figure of this title HN 777 has a couple of lambs peeping out from under her art deco style skirts. It would be difficult to imagine a ceramic portrayal of the nursery rhyme *Mary had a little lamb* without a lamb and of course HN 2048 included a lamb even if her dress is more contemporary than might be expected. An early figure, *Fruit Gathering* HN 449 also includes sheep appropriate when one remembers that it was common practice for farmers to graze sheep in their orchards. The windfalls providing food for the livestock whilst tidying the orchard at the same time. Naturally sheep appear with several of the numerous shepherds. *The Shepherd* HN 81 1st version and HN 1975 4th version together with *Lambing Time* HN 1890 all have woolly companions as does *The Shepherdess* HN 2990 from the *Reflections* series. The lamb also features in its symbolic role in the seasonal figures *Spring* HN 2085 and *Springtime* HN 3033.

Other aspects of farming are depicted such as feeding the chickens, a traditional chore for *The Farmers Wife* HN 2069, tending the geese, *Goose Girl* HN 425, and taking them to town to be sold on *Market Day* HN 1991, while the 1988 introduction *Country Maid* HN 3163 tends a young calf.

A countryside pursuit which today is apt to cause some controversy is hunting. Leaving aside the pros and cons of the subject *The Huntsman* HN 2492 although not attired in hunting-pink still makes a strong impression seated beside his favorite Foxhound.

Twilight HN 2256
Lambing Time HN 1890
Forty Winks HN 1974

Two figures evocative of the countryside are *The Gamekeeper* HN 2879 crouched beside his black Labrador gundog and *The Master* HN 2325, as shepherd, fondly stroking his faithful sheepdog.

The animals represented in the figurine range are not confined to the four-legged variety, birds of all kinds are found in profusion. Sailors are traditionally associated with birds and the connection is made in *Shore Leave* HN 2254 which shows a sailor home from the sea, with a feathered souvenir of some tropic isle perched on his shoulder. Perhaps the most famous parrot of all time, *Long John Silver's* 'Captain Flint' is of course in the same traditional pose in HN 2204.

Bunny HN 2214

Golden Days HN 2274

Stayed At Home HN 2207

My Pet HN 2238

The Seafarer HN 2455 has a less exotic feathered friend in the familiar Gull. Many pretty lady figurines are found with small birds perched in their hands. The majority of no identifiable variety, however it is quite obvious that *Esmeralda* HN 2168 holds a green Budgerigar and *Nichola* HN 2839 a Dove.

Some figurines feature more unusual animals, *Thanksgiving* HN 2446 has a large Turkey, *Lunchtime* HN 2485 and *Good Friends* HN 2783 are both feeding the rather rare red Squirrel and of course *The Organgrinder* HN 2173 has his Monkey. Some of the child studies have rather unusual animal friends. *Stayed at home* HN 2207 is a curly headed little girl clutching under her arm a chubby white pig. Less bizarre are *Affection* HN 2236 and *Bunny* HN 2214 both of which are nursing cuddly white rabbits.

Thanksgiving HN 2446

Organgrinder HN2173

Lunchtime HN 2485

Animals are found in the *Prestige* and *Limited Edition* models of which the most spectacular of all must be *Princess Badoura* HN 2081, a character in the Arabian Nights Entertainments. The Princess is riding on an elaborately bedecked elephant, one of the most dazzling of all the models in the collection, and the most expensive.

Robert Jefferson has included some exotic animals in the five groups he modelled for The *Myths and Maidens* series introduced in the 1980's. One of them *The Lady and the Unicorn* HN 2875 includes a mythical beast. They are all stories from Roman mythology. An earlier version of *Europa and the Bull* HN 95 was issued in 1918 but is rarely found today.

To mention every figure in the HN range which features an animal would make a very long chapter. If I have missed out your own particular favorite I apologise.

Within the HN figures range is the scope to build a fascinating collection using animals as the major theme. Such an assembly would stand as a collection in its own right or could as easily be an ajunct to a collection of animal models to which it would add variety of shape. In either case there is a veritable Royal Doulton Noah's Ark awaiting the collector.

THE FUTURE

Graham Tongue a talented animal modeller joined the Royal Doulton group in 1966. Since then he has modelled many horses, dogs and birds in the *BESWICK* range. Graham has always been a keen naturalist and enjoys the wildlife and the changing seasons when he takes his Collie, 'Jason' for an early morning walk. In the evening if he watches television, his pet Cockatoo 'Sadie', in one of her quieter moments, sits on his lap. He particularly loves horses and enjoys modelling them most of all. 'Red Rum', the popular racehorse, is his favorite because of his wonderful personality.

Graham tells how a racehorse or championship dog can take as long as five weeks to model. The animal has to be visited in stables or kennels and studied from life before an attempt is made to model it in the studio. Many visits are necessary as each individual animal has a particular expression and its own characteristics which must be captured. The stance must usually be a 'show' position so that the animal when viewed can be seen to advantage with four individually placed legs and the typical line to the head. The owners are consulted for their approval. Photographs can be an aid but are deceptive and not always reliable in bringing out the subtle individualities of each animal. The clay model must be made a twelth larger than the required finished size to allow for shrinkage in the kiln. You can see the difference in the size of the plaster model taken from the original representation of *Crinoline* by William Chance shown earlier. In fact Graham Tongue works in the same methods and to the same fine limits as his predecessors. When the model is completed to the artists satisfaction it leaves the studio to go before Royal Doulton's marketing board.

Modeller Graham Tongue works on the original clay sculpture of Barn Owl DA 1 with Betty the Barn Owl acting as his model. The piece took five weeks to model. Courtesy Lawley's By Post.

1990 heralds a new era in Royal Doulton animal production. Six prestigeous animals, *The Leopard, Tiger and Lion on the Rock, The Fighter Elephant*, another *Tiger* and a large *Fox* are all that remain in production of Charles Noke's original HN range. All others were discontinued in 1985. Animals were still made in the *Beswick* range but in 1989 that backstamp was discontinued. The *Beswick Connoisseur* range including all the horses, some cats and dogs and the *Fireside* models were given a *Royal Doulton* backstamp making this transition period into a nightmare for future animal catalogers.

1990 heralds a new Doulton animal range.

Graham Tongue and his studio have already completed the following models.

DA	1	Barn Owl	11	Graham Tongue 1990
Garden	2	Robin	6	Graham Tongue
Birds	3	Blue Tit	7	Martyn Alcock
Collection	4	Wren	5	Martyn Alcock
	5	Chaffinch	6	Warren Platt
	6	Hare	8.5	Warren Platt
The	7	Otter	9	Amanda Hughes
Wildlife	8	Badger	5.5	Amanda Hughes
Collection	9	Standing Fox	7.5	Warren Platt
	10	Fox with Cubs	6.5	Warren Platt
	11	Wood Mice	7.5	Amanda Hughes
All sizes include	12	Robin on Apple	6	Graham Tongue
wooden plinth	13	Blue Tit and Matchbox	7	Martyn Alcock
	40	Peregrine Falcon	11	Graham Tongue
	124	Desert Orchid	12	Graham Tongue Ltd Edit. 7500
	137	Barn Owl	7.5	Amanda Hughes

1990 proves a very appropriate date to publish the story of the HN range. Collectors can now correct me and we can complete the picture of the past whilst looking foward to new beginnings.

INDEX

BIBLIOGRAPHY

Royal Doulton 1815-1965. Desmond Eyles. Hutchinson 1975
The Doulton Burslem Wares. Desmond Eyles. Hutchinson 1980
Royal Doulton Figurines and Character Jugs. K. M. McClinton. USA 1978
Royal Doulton Figures. Desmond Eyles. Dennis 1978. 2nd Edtn 1987
Doulton Flambé Animals. Jocelyn Lukins 1981
Royal Doulton Bunnykins. Louise Irvine. Dennis 1984 (Bunnykin Figures)
Doulton Burslem Advertising Wares. Jocelyn Lukins. 1985
Doulton For The Collector. Jocelyn Lukins. PWC 1988
Collections - *The Sir Henry Doulton Museum*

STOP PRESS 1st August 1990

CONNOISSEUR SERIES

DA 15	*Arkle*	12"
16	*Nijinsky*	11
17	*Black Beauty* & foal	8
18	*Red Rum*	12.5
19	Hereford Bull	7.5
20	*Grundy*	11
21	Polled Hereford Bull	7.5
22	Life-Guard	14.5
23	Friesian Bull	7
24	Collie	8
25	Blues and Royals	14.5
26	Alsatian	9
27	Chardolais Cow and Calf	7
28	Morgan Horse	11.5
29	Friesian Cow	7.5
30	Friesian Cow and Calf	7.5
31	*The Minstrel*	13
32	Stag	13.5
33	Chardolais Cow and Calf	7
34	Hereford Cow and Calf	7
35	*Moonlight*	11
36	*Sunburst* (Palomino)	11
37	*Troy*	12
38	Pheasant	10.5
39	Cheetah on rock	6.5
40	Peregrine Falcon	11
*32	*The Majestic Stag*	15
*35	*Champion*	12.5
*38	*Open Ground*	12.5
*39	*The Watering Hole*	8

HORSES - Various finishes

DA 42	Race Horse *Bois Russell*	8
43	Shire	8.5
44	Horse	6
45	Trotting Horse	9
46	Mare	7
47	Shetland Pony	6
48	Horse	9
49	Palomino	9
50	Arab Xayal	6
51	Horse	7.5
52	Arab	7.5
53	Thoroughbred	8
55	Mare	5.5
56	Horse	5.5
57	*The Spirit of the Wind*	8
58	*The Spirit of Freedom*	7
59	*The Spirit of Youth*	7
60	*The Spirit of Fire*	8
61	*The Spirit of Earth*	7.5
62	Shire Horse	8
63	The Spirit of Peace	5
64	The Spirit of Affection	8
65	*Black Beauty*	7
66	*Black Beauty and foal*	6
68	Appaloosa	8
69	*Springtime* (foal)	5
70	*Young Spirit* (foal)	5
71	*Sunlight* (foal)	5
72	*Adventure* (foal)	5
73	*The Spirit of Adventure*	6
74-82	Foals (2 colours)	3-4"

FIRESIDE MODELS

83	Siamese Cat	14
84	Old English Sheepdog	11.5
85	Dalmation	14
86	Labrador (Golden & Black)	13.5
87	Yorkshire Terrier	10
88	Alsatian	14

DOGS Medium Size - two finishes

99	Rottweiler	5.5
100	Old English Sheepdog	5.5
101	Staffordshire Bull Terrier	4
102	Afghan Hound	5.5
103	Alsatian	6
104	Boxer	5.5
105	Doberman	5
106	Rough Collie	5.5
107	Springer Spaniel	5

SPIRIT DOGS

108	The Spaniel (3 colours)	8
109	The Setter (3 colours)	8.5
110	The Pointer	8.5
111	The Labrador (2 colours)	6.5
112	The Retriever	7.5

GOOD COMPANIONS

DA113	Pekinese	5.5
114	Norfolk Terrier	4
115	Poodle	5
116	Dachshund	4.5
117	Shetland Sheepdog	5
118	Cairn Terrier	4.5
119	Yorkshire Terrier	5
120	West Highland Terrier	5
121	King Charles Spaniel	5

CATS

122	Siamese Kitten	3
123	Kitten (3 colours)	3
124	Siamese Cat	7L
125	Siamese Cat	7L
126	Persian Cat (2 colours)	6
127	Siamese Cat	9
128	Persian Kitten	4
129	Siamese Cat	4
130	Siamese Cat	6.5
131	Black Cat	6.5
132	Persian (3 colours)	5

HORSE

134	Desert Orchid	12

BIRDS

137	Barn Owl	7.5
138	Kingfisher	9
139	Osprey	8

DOGS - Medium Size

141	Cocker Spaniel (2 colours)	4
142	Retriever (Golden)	5
143	Boarder Collie	4

* Duplicated numbers

Jocelyn Lukins, 14 Keith Grove,
London W12 9EZ

Typeset by J James, London. Printed by Bookmag, Scotland